To [handwritten]

'yogis'. [handwritten]

Lucia Harmeling [handwritten signature]

TRUST YOUR BODY, CHANGE YOUR LIFE

INTUITIVELY *full*

LUCIA HARMELING, MS, RDN, LD, RYT

ISBN: 978-1-7368090-8-2

Printed by Amazon KDP

Interior and Cover Design: Stephanie DuBois

Artist: Haley Bowen

Editor: Michelle Gean

For those doing the
expanding and heart-crushing work
of journeying back home to their body,
this is for you.

Acknowledgements

This book would not have been possible without the following people:

My number one fan and loving husband, Brett Harmeling. Thank you for always believing in my dreams and supporting me without hesitation. I love you more and more every day.

All the women who took the time to read, comment, and support me in my writing journey, thank you for being there when I needed you the most: Susan Swann, Kristen Porter, Haley Garcia, Alexa Shank, Maria Pia Turner, Cecilia Hisse, Stephanie DuBois, Haley Bowen, Michelle Gean, and Prim Ormanovich.

My future children, thank you for inspiring me to heal so that one day I could house and nourish you within me. For this, I am forever grateful.

To God and every human being who deepened my relationship with Christ, thank you for helping me along in my journey.

To Lightyear Leadership, for supporting me in creating big goals and a life I love.

Table of Contents

Introduction

I struggled with food and my body for years. Counting and controlling what I ate was my whole world. I know what it's like to feel trapped in your own world and thoughts. I *also* know what it's like to break free from those self-limiting, destructive thoughts and patterns and *finally* start living. Now, having escaped from my misery, I see how much laughter, connection, fun, life-giving conversations, and satisfying meals I missed. *Shrinking myself made me smaller, and it made the life I was living smaller too.*

I want you to know it's possible to care for your body and not obsess about it. It's possible to feel at home in your skin. It's possible to not overthink every ounce of food you eat. It's possible not to spend days in front of the mirror tearing apart every part of your being. You are more than your body. You are the light that resides within your beautiful soul and illuminates every act of love and care you share with the world. Trusting your body doesn't come from changing it. It comes from respecting it.

I'll be the first to admit that I'm not some guru or a masterful, enlightened saint of a woman. I am flawed, imperfect, and always growing. Perfection is not the purpose. What I am, however, is a registered dietitian and certified intuitive eating coach who understands what it's like to be in the trenches of a disordered relationship with food; I understand what it takes to choose to heal.

In connecting with hundreds, if not thousands, of women over the years, what I know to be true is this: We *all* have insecurities and limiting-thought tapes running through our heads – fears and longings – yet we think we are alone.

In my journey, I always felt completely alone. It wasn't until I started sharing my story that I began to sense connection and see the purpose my food struggles were playing in my life. The more I shared, the bigger my heart grew, and the more I allowed myself to heal. I learned there is power in vulnerability and connection. There is power in being me and sharing my story.

God made *us*, not someone else, for a reason. We were made to be ourselves. We were made to be heard and seen and felt exactly as we are. There is no need to be someone else. The space we take up is on purpose and *has a purpose*. Let that sink in.

When we live our life striving to be someone else or to have a different body, we lose sight of who we are. We lose our raw beauty and the limitless power that resides within us. We lose our sense of purpose and divine grace.

God knew when creating the human body – a carefully and craftily made mystery – we would need a little guidance and support, which is why He gave us our intuition, our strongest and most valuable sense of knowing. Our intuition is His sweet whisper into our soul. It is our guide. When we trust our body, we trust God. When we trust God, we change our lives. Our body knows what we need and will remind us of that as much as it can. When we don't listen, it'll do everything it can to bring us back on track. It is constantly looking out for us and keeping us safe. It is innately intelligent.

As soon as I started trusting my intuition, everything in my life started changing in a way I didn't even think was possible. If you're even a bit like me and feel a need to control your life, I get it, and I see you. It can be hard to let go and trust, but the minute you start doing it, you'll wonder why you never allowed yourself to do it before. Let this book be a sweet reminder that you are not meant to be in control; you are meant to be divinely guided.

To any woman who has ever struggled with food and her body, I'm here to tell you that there's more to life than spending your time wishing your body were different or spending every waking hour wanting to control it or fully understand it. We aren't meant for that, but at times, it's so easy to doubt our ability to know, feel, sense, and decide what is right for our life. It's so easy to get lost or feel trapped and confused by other's opinions. It's so easy to feel like we are not ourselves, yet simultaneously have no idea how to get back to who we truly are. I am writing this book *for you*, which is likely why you've picked it up or how it somehow made its way into your life. Nothing happens by accident. You are reading this at exactly the right time for you.

While reading this book, I encourage you to pause, check in, pray, meditate, be in silence, and start listening for what your intuition and body sensations are telling you. My hope is that out of all the stories in this book you find the one for you. It might be a sentence or a full story, but no matter which it is, I hope you find healing, curiosity, and joy – trusting that, as you read, your journey is taking a new turn. I invite you to read with your eyes, yet listen deeply with your heart. You will know when something serves you and when it doesn't, when something feels right, deep within your bones, and when it doesn't. Your intuition is there, always guiding you toward the words meant just for you, and when you find those words, your eyes will widen and pause, your whole body will shift slightly back, and your heart will deepen. Those sensations are God's gentle whisper echoing into your soul; it is your intuition. Allow yourself to feel and hear it. You may not know quite yet what shift you'll get in your life, but you *will* feel it. Trust the process. Happy reading!

With love,
Lu

p.s. This book is a compilation of my own stories and experiences. It is intended to create connection, not to provide therapy. All the views here are my own and should not be used as a framework for healing. This book is not a substitute for medical treatment nor should it replace individualized nutrition counseling. If you or someone you know is struggling with disordered eating, an eating disorder, or any mental health related condition, reach out to a trained professional.

Chapter 1

To Gain, We Must First Lose

At age 15, I lost all joy in eating. At age 16, I lost my period and all my friends. At age 17, I lost my social life and confidence. I lost my freedom to choose and my sense of adventure.

My eating disorder took a lot from me. The first things it took were my ability to focus, my drive to study, and my passion for learning. My mind was so focused on counting every calorie that I no longer prioritized what was once important to me. Without all this loss, I wouldn't understand my body as well as I do now. If I hadn't had experiences that shook me and left me feeling raw and lost, I wouldn't have found myself within the darkness. The extreme pain, sadness, and hurt have led me to find more balance over the years. They've led me to find myself. If I hadn't lost the things I loved and wanted so badly, I wouldn't have awakened to the reality of the life I had been living.

I distinctly remember the day I found out I didn't match into Texas A&M University, the thing that I wanted the most as a high schooler. I was wasting time in my computer class, going back and forth debating whether I should eat another red and white Starlight mint or not. That's how much thought I put into what I ate. I had just gotten word that A&M had sent out their next round of acceptance and rejection letters, but even before I logged into my student portal, I had a gut feeling the news wouldn't be good. I could feel my stomach churning and my heart sinking deeper and deeper into my chest.

A&M had already sent out thousands of acceptance letters a month or two before, and I hadn't received one. There was a part of me that knew the answer; my gut knew. My brain, though, was holding onto every last bit of hope that I would get into the school of my dreams. I went through all the reasons in my head as to why my letter hadn't come in yet: *They had a lot of applicants this year. If I wouldn't have made it, they would have told me sooner.*

I sat there wondering if I should sign in or wait until I was home alone with no one else around. I got nauseated and felt a rush of anxiety move through my bones. I HAD TO KNOW...and I had to know *now*. I had to fiercely rip off the not-knowing BAND-AID right then and there. Waiting and anticipating is sometimes worse than finding out the truth.

As I took a deep breath, I felt my shoulders tighten up toward my ears and my shoulder blades stiffened as if they were cementing themselves into my upper back, never to be separated again. My teeth clenched and my entire upper body floated up two inches higher toward my computer screen. As I started typing in my username and password, I prayed. I took a deep breath and signed in. The screen blinked, and there it was staring right at me.

I didn't get in. Tears flooded my eyes. *The answer was no.*

My heart sank right into my stiff chest. I wish I had known *then* that every rejection is simply a redirection. But in that moment, no ounce of positivity or forward thinking would have made a difference. Looking back, this was one of the most transformational moments of my life. This was my redirection; this was God guiding me back to my path.

I was paralyzed. I didn't know if I should allow the tears to flow down my face, say something to the girl sitting next to me (who had been accepted to A&M), or run right out the door. Within the next twenty seconds, I did all of that, racing to the nearest bathroom.

As soon as I made it to the bathroom, dense warm tears started rolling down my face. It was the kind of crying that left my face red, my eyes puffy, and my skin itchy and damp. All I wanted to do was cry, to shrink so small into myself that nothing could harm me. My heart was slowly tearing open inside. I didn't want anyone to see me like this. I wished I could be teleported out of the cold, dirty bathroom stall – with no comfortable place to lean – straight into my cozy, warm bed.

I heard the loud ringing of the bell and instantly felt some relief. Everyone would be rushing to lunch. That was my chance to escape unseen. I waited for the hallways to clear and rushed back to my desk where I had left all my belongings. I grabbed my light pink Jansport backpack and textbooks and headed home. I had never been the kind of person to skip class, but in that moment, nothing phased me. The minute I walked out of the loud, large side doors of my high school, a layer of shame started peeling off of my body. Thank God it was Friday and I would have a few days without seeing my classmates. I didn't want anyone to know. *How would I face my friends on Monday?*

Do you want to know the real reason I didn't get into A&M on my first try? It wasn't because I wasn't capable or smart enough. It was because my focus had been on shrinking my body instead of growing my potential. My eating disorder had taken over my focus. I spent all my time counting calories so that I would stay small. I hadn't yet realized that in doing this, I was giving up the life I wanted. That's all diets and eating disorders do for you. They make *you* small. They rob you of your ability to thrive while leaving you with a false sense of control that temporarily satisfies an undernourished body.

When we physically shrink ourselves, we shrink our lives.

That day was devastating, and it was also one of the first times I remember binging, eating in excess until I physically couldn't eat anymore, and feeling totally out of control.

The next day, in an effort to cheer me up, my sister who was attending A&M at the time, had my boyfriend bring me a chocolate cake on her behalf. Food was one of the ways I grew up feeling comfort. My mom cooked and baked my whole life so having food made for me, or brought to me, made me feel seen and taken care of. I still, to this day, enjoy showing and receiving love in this way. Finding comfort in food is not wrong, though, it can and might be taken to an extreme when an unhealthy relationship with food is present...as it was for me.

As soon as my boyfriend walked in with the chocolate cake and told me it was from my sister, my eyes lit up. I reached over to my red Nokia cell phone and called her immediately. As soon as I heard her voice, I got emotional. A sense of connection seeped deep into my bones. There she was, even when she couldn't be there.

Isn't it beautiful how food can bring us comfort and connection even during the saddest and hardest times?

Receiving that cake initially made me feel loved and connected, but it quickly turned into discomfort. Just like that, my disordered brain took a beautiful moment of connection and turned it into a fearful nightmare. *What am I supposed to do with a whole chocolate cake? Ew, gross, there's no way I can eat that. Ugh, what do I do with it now? Maybe I can get everyone else to eat it? Ugh, why'd she have to give me a chocolate cake? Doesn't she know I don't want that?*

A few hours later, I lost "control." It was late in the evening. My boyfriend had already left and I'd barely eaten dinner. I waited until everyone was upstairs to make my way downstairs and into the kitchen. I hated eating around other people because it made me feel like I had less control over what I was eating and therefore couldn't eat freely. I also hated the thought of other people watching me eat, especially if it was a food I considered "off-limits." All my thoughts about what happened felt overwhelming.

I got to the kitchen, dimmed the kitchen lights, and looked over at the island. There I was. Alone. The whole chocolate cake, untouched, was waiting for me. I quietly tiptoed over to one of the tall, wooden bar stools and took a seat. It made a small creaking noise which I hoped no one had heard. I could feel my mouth watering. Hundreds of thoughts flooded my brain. Guilt. Shame. Fear. Failure.

The thought of serving myself a whole slice of cake felt overwhelming, so instead, I decided it made more sense to pick at it with a fork. I grabbed a fork and popped open the cake's loud plastic covering.

Y'all why is that covering so loud?! I'm sure even my neighbors knew I was eating cake.

I took the first bite. Then a second. Then a third. Followed by a fourth. The more bites I took, the faster I ate. Not even ten minutes in, I was a fourth of the way into the cake. *What was happening? Why couldn't I stop? Why was I now busting out the ice cream too? Screw it. I'm already this far in, I might as well eat the rest.*

Even though I ate half the cake, I don't remember enjoying any of it. My emotions and my taste buds were numb. I could see and hear all the sad thoughts running through my head, but because my mouth and stomach were distracted, I wasn't allowing myself to feel and process them.

Until I stopped eating.

As soon as I did, I felt as if I had swallowed a bowling ball. My stomach was hard and dense. I hadn't felt full, and specifically *this* full, in such a long time. It was overwhelming.

What had I done?

Not only was I physically uncomfortable to the point of feeling sick, but I was also emotionally full. The sad thoughts I had about not getting into my dream school had been temporarily numbed while eating, but they came back with a vengeance. I started crying. Minutes later, my mom came downstairs and saw that I'd eaten half the cake. She didn't say much, but I could tell she was partially happy that I'd eaten. I, however, felt that same feeling you feel when someone catches you doing something you don't want them to know about. I felt a tingle down my spine and an instant shrugging in my stomach as if my organs were twisting up into each other. Not only had I *not* gotten into my dream school and would have to give up the future I had so clearly seen for myself, but I also felt like everything else in me was crumbling. I felt broken. My stomach felt distended and dense, and the rest of me felt empty and numb.

This was just the first glimpse of many emotional binges I'd experience throughout my college and young adult years. Each one left me feeling emptier, more broken, and fully disgusted with myself.

Little did I know that binges were my body's way of responding to restriction, both psychologically and physically. Each time I was lacking nourishment, my body would try to fill me up. My body was doing everything it could to keep me alive and safe. I didn't realize it then, but each of those moments were red flags waving in the wind, begging for my attention: *Lucia, there is something wrong. We can't keep doing this.*

Our body always knows exactly how to bring us back into balance, even when it feels like it's out of control and nothing is making sense. Everything is happening for a reason. There's a bigger picture. It's not our job to understand and make sense of every little thing our body is doing, but it *is* our responsibility to be aware, slow down, and listen to our body's nudges, our inner self, our intuition.

Sometimes, to gain trust in ourselves again, we must first experience losing it.

The moments that change our life are oftentimes our hardest moments.

They are there to guide us. Each time we feel lost or out of control in our own body or life, it is simply an opportunity to ask ourselves what there is to learn and what our next step will be. These are our pivotal moments – the ones that help us find ourselves again.

Chapter 2

Body Changes Are Weird

It was in middle school that I started to question if I was beautiful. *Did people think I was pretty? Did I measure up?* Before then, I'm sure I thought about how I looked to other people but never to the extent that I had while in middle school. Those were the years when puberty started, not just for me but for everyone around me. My boobs hadn't come in yet, but it felt like 90% of the girls in my class already had theirs. The pressure to be beautiful. To be noticed. To be liked. It was all there. Suddenly, bodies were something that were talked about freely. The girls talked about them. The guys talked about them. The cool girls rolled their skirts up to show more leg, wore padded, cute Victoria's Secret bras, and knew exactly how to flirt with the more athletic guys in class.

Then there was me: sweaty armpits, small boobs, greasy hair. My hormones hadn't gotten the 411 on what they were supposed to be doing, at least what I was hoping they would do: make me look good. Mine liked to do the opposite. I could've counted on one hand how many times I felt beautiful then. Even though I didn't think I was pretty enough, my body felt neutral. It wasn't something I focused on or worked on changing. Looking back, I think I liked it, other than my ridiculously sweaty armpits. Having those was tough. I would walk around school as if my arms were glued to the sides of my body. I'd never fully raise my hand in class. I'd even wear a thick sweatshirt in the heat of the summer just to hide my large sweat rings — the last thing I wanted was for someone to see them.

Even though my body felt awkward, my eating felt free. I didn't care what my snack labels said. I had no idea how many calories I needed nor did I care. Exercise was the last thing on my mind. I hated gym class and moving my body because it made me feel sweatier and even more uncoordinated than I already was. While my P.E. class ran laps around the field, I hid behind the baseball fence, hoping I wouldn't get caught even though I always did. Who knew that a see-through, wire fence wouldn't quite cover up a whole individual? Go figure.

Ohhhh, middle school.

Because I had grown up with brothers, I was used to being around people who would eat everything in sight and *more*. I never thought to question how much I ate or how fast I ate until I was over at my best friend's house one night. They had ordered pizza. We were upstairs watching a movie, all curled between blankets and sleeping bags laughing our butts off. As I reached over for my third slice of pizza, my friend gave me a look. "Dang, Lucia, you eat a lot..." I looked over at her plate: she had barely finished her first slice. I felt embarrassed. *Was I eating too much? Why was my hunger so different from hers? Was I not supposed to be enjoying pizza this much?*

At that moment, I felt seen, but not in a good way. I definitely did **not** feel beautiful or ladylike.

I never felt like being me was enough. I always felt different, sloppy, and messy. My mind was always looking for evidence that I didn't fit in. My mom and sister would always remind me of how beautiful I was, and every time they did, I felt better. My heart would warm and my mind would feel at peace. I needed those moments of reassurance to help me feel like I was okay.

Fast forward to high school. This was the first time I felt like my body was being scrutinized by other people. I knew I had wide hips and large boobs, but boys were starting to point it out, and instead of being flattered, I felt weird about it. *Ummm hello, can y'all stop staring, please?* I didn't like being looked at and I hated that my body was getting so much attention. I felt like an item that didn't want to be on display.

I remember walking out of Home Ed class wearing my red, baggy sweatpants with the word *lacrosse* boldly printed down my left pant leg. As I walked out of the classroom, I felt someone checking me out. You know, that energy when you suddenly feel eyes piercing one part of your body as if someone is shining a spotlight on it? I turned halfway around and saw a guy with an athletic build standing a few feet behind me. He came up to me laughing and wrapped his muscular arm around my shoulder.

"Gurl, you fine. What do you do?!" he asked as he looked straight down at my butt.

I laughed awkwardly and shrugged my shoulders "*...uh lacrosse? I don't know.*"

I don't quite remember what he said next. He probably told me to keep playing.

Was I supposed to feel flattered? Ashamed? Think it was funny? Be proud of it?

Shortly after, it became a story my friends and I laughed about. I mean, I *knew* I had a big butt. To this day, it's probably the one thing about my body that people comment on the most. If you ask my husband, it's the first thing he noticed about me *(which still makes me laugh)*.

However, back in high school, as much as it was funny, it was also comments like those that made me MUCH more hyper-aware and self-conscious about my body. From all my struggles with body image and food, I can now honestly say that no body comment is ever fully a compliment, even when it's meant to be. The time I was most complimented on my body was when I was at my lowest weight.

Note: lowest, NOT healthiest. I was malnourished and underfed, yet I continued to be praised for it.

You might be reading this and thinking, "I don't mind compliments." I'm not saying compliments are wrong, but what I am saying is that there *is* a major difference between compliments like, "Wow, you look beautiful" versus "Hey, have you lost weight!? You look great!" The latter example ties our ability to be accepted to the physical space our body takes up. This can easily be interpreted to mean, *"Now that I'm smaller, I look better than I did."* This "compliment" reinforces that our body was not good enough before it changed. It creates a new standard to keep up, and it's usually not a realistic one.

If we receive compliments praising us for our weight loss, our mind subconsciously starts to wonder how we look to others.

Does that mean that before I lost weight I didn't look great?

Does that mean that to continue to look great I'll have to stay at this weight?

Am I more desirable now that I lost weight?

Imagine you're engaging in behaviors such as not eating when you're hungry, forcing yourself to work out X number of hours a day, avoiding all social outings to avoid unplanned calories or foods, or not attending any events that would disrupt the workout routine you have planned. What happens *then* when someone praises your body? Is it still helpful?

Probably not. *For me, it wasn't.* Body compliments not only left me feeling uncomfortable and more focused on my body, but they also kept me rooted in my unhealthy behaviors, believing that if I deviated from my "structure," my body would drastically change making me less desirable.

Body compliments do not support recovery or a normal relationship with food. They support disorder, whether we are currently struggling or not.

There are so many other things to focus on. Controlling our body shouldn't be one of them. Our body is **meant to change** so putting energy toward resisting the change is counterproductive and draining. Body changes aren't always comfortable but, then again, what changes are?

Back in high school, all I knew was that I **hated** all the unexpected body changes. I had first learned about the changes a woman's body goes through in middle school, but no one had ever talked to me about what these changes would *feel* like. These are two very different things. It's like spending time reading about how to do a handstand versus throwing your legs around trying to nail one. The active option is messier.

I liked being in control and was an overachiever since day one. I grew up in a structured, seven-person Catholic family where my parents were fearless in the pursuit of their dreams. They never stepped down from a challenge and always believed they could overcome whatever was put in their path. They wanted the best for us, so we were always encouraged to do our best and *be our best*. As much as this served me in some areas of my life, it also fueled and contributed to my anxiety. Striving for perfection would only leave me with momentary satisfaction because I was stuck trying to prove my worth through external validation. I'd reach a goal, celebrate it, and then wonder what was next. Nothing ever felt like it was enough. *I never felt like I was good enough.* This led to a lot of comparison and competition, neither of which would serve me well in my eating journey or my relationship with food.

In comparing ourselves to others, we will always fall short because we are not meant to be another human being. There will always be something someone else has or does that we don't – and that's okay. We are meant to be different and yet strive to be the best version of ourselves, which is not tied to how we eat or how we look. I didn't understand this back then, but I do now. Living in comparison robs us of compassion and it robs us of the

13

ability to grow into ourselves.

From a young age, I was taught to respect my body. I was taught modesty and that my body was not something to be openly shared. This always resonated with me. It made sense that not every part of my body was meant to be shared with the world. However, I also now know that putting so much attention on covering up specific body parts made me more self-conscious about them. If I were wearing something tighter than usual, I felt uncomfortable, as if I were doing something wrong. To this day, I still remember the comment my grandmother made when I was ten years old. I was getting into our family van when she paused and looked over at me, then at my mother, and then back at me. "Lucia, don't you think that skirt is a little too tight for Mass?" The same black skirt I had worn for two years was now suddenly tightly hugging my expanding and growing hips. *Did I do something wrong? Were my hips a problem?* I felt embarrassed and attacked.

Sometimes I wonder if part of the body shame I experienced as an adult came from being extra careful that my curvy figure didn't show. I spent years buying clothes a size too big just to make sure nothing hugged my body.

My body was changing: stretch marks, swollen breasts, wider thighs, a softer mid-section, pimples, and sweatier armpits. It was in complete control, and there was nothing I could do about it. I was a mess, or at least it felt that way.

When our body changes, it's normal to question the change: to sit back and wonder what in the world is going on. Even though my body knew exactly what it was doing by growing into its adult shape, to me, it felt unexpected and awkward. I didn't like it.

I still remember standing naked on the edge of our bathroom's pink bathtub, facing our bathroom mirror. I could see my body changing. I could see the curves coming in and my body expanding. Part of me was intrigued by it, the other part of me was weirded out. *Who was this person?*

I would look at myself in the mirror and think, "Wow, I'm becoming a woman." My body was becoming less of what I was used to and more of what I was seeing in other women in our society: curves, hips, and breasts.

In high school, my anxiety and need for comparison seeped its way into an already complicated relationship with my body and food. I felt frustrated with my shape and the extra fat I deemed as "bad."

I started controlling food as a way of telling myself that I was in control. If I could meticulously count and track every single calorie that entered my body, my anxious energy would dissipate. It would make me feel like everything else in my life was in control and like nothing could phase me.

At the time, I didn't notice or understand the harm I was causing with food nor the dependent relationship I was fostering. I knew something was off; but, the ability to have a sense of control in my life felt exciting and addicting. I had control over what I put in my mouth, and through that, I felt empowered. Little did I know that my body would soon start rebelling – just as it was made to – to keep me alive.

Chapter 3

Going Against the Flow

I remember the day I FINALLY got my period. I had always wondered when it would be my turn. I was in high school, but I might as well have been 35. That's what it felt like, anyway, since I got it so much later than pretty much *every* other girl I knew.

I was in my room packing up to go on a Catholic weekend retreat in California. I had never traveled without my family which made me nervous, yet also really excited. I went to the bathroom, sat on the toilet to pee, and immediately freaked out.

What in the heck was in my underwear?

Surely, something was wrong with me. There was brown, thick liquid coming out of me. In my head, it looked like tar.

Oh no. This isn't good.

I've never peed so fast in my life! I ran out of the bathroom to find my mom. "*Mami, there's something wrong with me! There's brown, thick stuff coming out of me.*" My mom laughed, smiled, and said "*LUUU!!!! You got your period!*"

"*No, Mami, it's not blood. I think there's something wrong with me.*"

"*Ay Lucia....it's your period.*"

"*Well, can you PLEASE come see!? I need to be sure.*"

My mom walked into the bathroom with me. With a look of disgust on my face, I showed her what was in my underwear. It *was* my period. No one had ever told me what it would be like to get my period for the first time.

What was my body DOING and why doesn't it just look like normal red flowing blood?

Nobody tells you this stuff: how sometimes it's deep red, sometimes it's dark brown, and sometimes there are blood boogers – aka blood clots. Not cute, but so real. As much as I had been waiting to *finally* get my period, did it have to come NOW? Of *all* times. How was I supposed to get through a weekend retreat *and* figure out this whole pad situation?

How would I know when to change it? Can people see my pad through my clothes? Will they think I'm wearing a diaper? What if guys notice?

Fear crept in.

What if it's not my period and there's something wrong with me and I'm stuck in the middle of nowhere with no one else I know? Even though my mom reassured me I was fine and that the way my period came in was normal, I was still weirded out. It wasn't what I had imagined.

I don't know what your first period experience was like, but for me, it was *very weird.* My body was suddenly doing something new that it had never done before and it made me uncomfortable. I had no idea what it was doing, yet according to my mom and the 6th-grade period talk I'd sat through, it was normal. Our body does so much we don't understand.

I always had a pretty funky relationship with my cycle. Before I got my period, I wanted it. Once I had it, I hated it. Two and a half years later, when it decided to disappear on me, I would've given anything for it to come back. I would get jealous and feel left out when I would hear other girls complaining about their cramps, cravings, and bloating. I wanted to be able to ask, "Do you have an extra tampon?" I wanted to be that person. I wanted to be and feel included. Not having a period for years made me feel like I wasn't good enough to fit in with the other girls. *Why wouldn't my body just work like everyone else's? Why couldn't I experience the same things and talk about the same things everyone else was talking about?*

The first two years of having a cycle, my body was still trying to figure itself out. I wasn't getting a consistent period every month. Sometimes I'd skip a month. Other times, I'd bleed enough to scare myself. I still remember the horrible day back in high school when I leaked through my clothes for the very first time. Of course, it happened during the most awkward time of my life: sophomore year of high school, to be exact. I was stuck in geometry class in the middle of Mrs. T's boring lecture when suddenly, I looked down and saw blood on my seat.

Oh shit. This isn't good.

It makes me laugh to think that I wasn't aware that *at some point* a pad stops holding liquid. DUH, Lucia, the liquid has to go somewhere. They aren't meant to hold liquid forever.

I had gone almost all day at school without changing my pad.
Gross, I know.

Looking back, I was so uncomfortable being on my period that the thought of having to change my pad at school made me feel even more awkward, so I avoided it. I was nervous about not changing it correctly, spending too long in the bathroom, and then getting in trouble for it, or even worse...being late to class which I *hated*. I wasn't the kind of person to walk in late, especially if it meant walking into a full classroom where everyone's attention immediately went to the door as soon as it opened. ***Not my idea of high school fun.***

Our geometry teacher was wrinkly and moody. Her long, colored nails made a high-pitched, irritating tapping sound as they lightly made contact with the overhead projector. Her makeup was always something that caught my attention. Her rotating eyeshadow and eyeliner colors were fuchsia pink, metallic blue, and bright purple. She reminded me of a modern-day witch with her soft, rough voice and creepy stare.

If anyone asked, *"Ummm, wait...I missed that, can we go back?"*

She'd look over at them with her big eyes, expressionless for what felt like minutes.

"Uh...never mind. I think I got it."

She was also the kind of teacher who had trust issues about students leaving her classroom to go anywhere, especially the restroom. "You can't go unless it's an emergency!"

Okay, lady, ummm no. Let me go when I need to go. Why does it have to be an emergency? I mean our school had enough troublemakers to make most teachers suspicious, but still, **I was the good kid**. *Why couldn't awkward me be trusted?*

There I was, sitting in your typical hard, orange-colored chair with a metal pole to the right of me that attached to a small wooden (but probably actually plastic) desk. All through class, I could feel something coming out of me as if my body were slowly pulsating liquid out. Beautiful imagery, I know.

My pad felt full, a little *too* full. We were midway into a lecture about shapes and angles when I suddenly felt something cold under my upper leg. *Ummm, that's odd.* Chills ran from the crown of my head to the very tips of my toes. My face got warm. I looked down, slid my thigh over, and *saw it.*

There was blood, **my blood**, ON. MY. SEAT. *Holy crap! What now?*

I started sweating and probably turned ten shades whiter, which is pretty white for me given that I'm already pretty pale. I shot my hand up into the air, made eye contact with my teacher, and before she even had a chance to ask me anything, I shouted out, "I have to go to the restroom...

IT'S AN EMERGENCY."

I'm sure it was either the panic in my eyes or the fact that I usually didn't speak up in class that kept her from questioning me. Thank goodness I had a sweatshirt with me. I wrapped it around my waist and jumped out of my chair while simultaneously throwing a textbook onto my seat. You know, *totally casual.*

To this day, I still have NO idea if my class was staring at me or still paying attention to our grumpy teacher. In my mind, every single person's eyes were on me as I ran out of there totally frazzled. I speed-walked through our wide, never-ending, red-locker-framed hallways until I made it to the restroom. I went into one of the stalls and hovered over the toilet. I have never again to this day seen a pad more soaked than that one. I was amazed and also disgusted at how much my body could bleed in just a few hours. The feeling of relief as I changed my pad helped every muscle in my tense body soften as I let out a gentle sigh. The bell rang. I rushed out of the bathroom and headed back to the now-empty classroom. *Thank goodness! I can't even begin to imagine walking back into a classroom I'd just run out of with visible bloodstains on my butt.* Not my proudest moment. My teacher didn't say a word as I grabbed my books and headed out the door, sweatshirt still tightly wrapped around my waist.

Saved by the bell...and my sweatshirt.

Let's be real, I'm still traumatized about leaking. I mean, c'mon, who wants bloodstains on their butt? No one. Sometimes, allowing our body to do what it needs to do gets crazy messy, especially when we are not used to it and have no idea how to react or take care of ourselves. But that's how we learn. Our body knows what it's doing. It's usually our mind that doesn't.

I wish I had understood back then that it's normal for periods to be heavier in the beginning. In our teen years, our body's reproductive system is waking up, and it takes time for our body to figure itself out and find its rhythmic flow.

Here is the truth, I didn't give my body a chance to find normalcy. Of course periods are wacky in the beginning. Out of nowhere, our body starts bleeding every month. It's new and different and *our body needs time and grace to figure itself out.* I never really gave it that opportunity. In just two years, I went from having heavy, leaking periods to no periods at all. Zip. Zero. None.

After I got my period, my body continued to change. In what felt like a span of just a few months, I was in a completely different body. I didn't feel like me. Add hormones, pimples, and the pressures of wanting to fit in and it made perfect sense why I wanted to be back in the body I knew, or at least back in a body that I perceived was more comfortable. I wasn't ready for my body to change. I wasn't ready for any of it.

Several things triggered my first diet: the need for perfection, the need for approval, and my desire to have some sense of control since my body felt so out of whack. Dieting was a result of being uncomfortable in my own skin and feeling like everything around me was changing. I needed something to ground me and make me feel safe. Then along came dieting with all its false promises.

Two years after I started my period, my body went straight into survival mode. A combination of not eating enough, exercising too much, and already having irregular cycles led my period to say goodbye. For **years.** Why would my body put any energy into having a cycle when it barely had enough energy to keep the rest of my body working well?

At the time, dieting in high school was seen as a trendy thing to do. It was during this time that diets like the Special K diet became popular. The Special K diet emphasized replacing two meals with two bowls of cereal and supplementing with protein shakes along with one or two of their low-calorie bars. It was essentially a way to become dependent on their products. All diets were like that, getting you to buy into their pills, powders, shakes, and rules. Even while being on the dieting bandwagon, something in me knew that all these diets were a scam. Because I never took part in an advertised one, I deemed my kind of dieting "normal." I was just "watching what I was eating" and "moving more," which was the exact thing that ended up slipping me right into my eating disorder. Diets are tricky like that. One minute, we think we're just being mindful; the next minute we're questioning everything we eat.

Back then, and even to this day, eating less or being on a diet to "watch my figure" was a way of joining in on a conversation with other women. It created connection. I could suddenly talk to other women about which foods they were avoiding and how "bad" we had been if we'd eaten something that was "not allowed" or was "off-limits." Sadly, the connection was based on tearing ourselves down. *Who was struggling more?*

Dieting also made me believe that if I were smaller, I'd suddenly be liked. I'd be cooler. Prettier. More desirable. I'd achieve more things. I started to see losing weight as the magical key I needed to solve all my problems. I'd eat less, suddenly lose weight, and get more attention. It *seemed* easy, yet was a total lie.

Months before I decided to start dieting, my older sister had started watching what she was eating. She had lost weight and was receiving compliments. "Oh, you look so beautiful." "You look great." "You're so small." At that same time, my body had been slowly changing to find its natural adult size: my boobs were bigger, my hips were wider, my face felt fuller.

I still remember that early Saturday afternoon when I was sitting at the kitchen counter having a snack with a friend. My friend looked over at me, wide-eyed, and tapped my thighs.

"Woah, they're *so* big."

"....Um, yeah, it's muscle."

"Ha! No, it's **fat**."

My heart sank so low that my heart rate might as well have been negative. My jaw tightened and my eyes widened. I had never, until that moment, thought of myself as *fat*.

I didn't know what to say. She giggled, and we changed the subject.

My greatest fear – of not being accepted, especially by my friends – became real. As soon as my friend went home, I immediately ran up the stairs to find my mom.

"Mami, am I fat?"

My mom looked confused, "Why are you asking me that?"

"My friend said I was."

"Lucia, you aren't fat, but you have gained some weight."

My face filled with tears. My jaw unclenched. I was suddenly VERY aware of my lower body and the weight that it was carrying. At that moment, it was as if my legs had turned into heavy, thick, cement blocks. I walked away feeling like I had done something wrong; I felt like all the fun and joy I was having eating foods with my high school friends had somehow gotten "out of control." *What had I done? How had I let myself get like this? And why hadn't anyone told me sooner?* In my eyes, I had made myself not belong. I had created a flaw.

I went into a downward spiral of tears and sadness all because I interpreted the word "fat" to mean failure. I made it mean I was damaged, even though I wasn't. It's moments like these that shock us and leave a profound ache in our hearts and in our bones. My friend wasn't trying to hurt me. She was simply regurgitating what she had heard as a young girl living in a diet-centered, fat-shaming world. It's sad to think that from such a young age, we are all brought up in a world hearing that our body shape needs to be controlled and that when, and if, our body changes, it should only change to look like the thin, ideal that our society praises.

Honestly, it wouldn't have mattered if my mom had said something different. All I had heard growing up was that fat was not good. It's sad to think a simple word could've had such a negative and large impact on my life. I gave that word so much power and meaning that it spiraled me right into a food and body prison for years.

How did a normal word become such an insult in our world?

It wasn't long after that day that I decided I'd go on a diet. As soon as I made the decision, I felt a sense of control. I could do this. I could feel love and acceptance again. I would be the one to decide what my body would look like. My body wouldn't win. I would.

"I'll show them. I can be small and pretty too."

Being 16 years old, I knew nothing about dieting or working out. All I had heard was that eating less and moving more were the "keys" to getting smaller. In my mind, they were the keys to regaining my sense of worthiness, my beauty, and my need to feel and be accepted as a woman.

My first diet started by subtly limiting foods. I would forego the delicious side of french fries, or avoid the warm toasted bun on my burger. I now know that this is usually how a disordered relationship with food and our body starts. A diet is one of the slipperiest and nastiest slopes right into disordered eating or an eating disorder. One minute you're cutting back a bit; the next minute you are cutting out entire food groups and feel like everything is off limits. What's even worse is that instead of "gaining control," I lost it. I lost the natural connection and awareness of what my body needed. I lost total trust in my body and in myself. It was that dangerous.

My diet was so limited that it got to a point where I was eating so little. I wouldn't even consider feeding a toddler how little I was eating. Not only was I barely nourishing myself, but I also started adding in more exercise. My hour and a half long lacrosse practices were no longer enough. I now found myself mindlessly walking on our treadmill. I would fill my day with movement and activities because I had convinced myself that if I did, it would be harder to overeat or gain weight. Movement was consuming my mind, shutting down my body, and numbing me from my life.

All I could think about was my next meal and how I'd make it through without eating too much. Each time I finished a meal, I would already be thinking about my next one and how many mints or pieces of gum I'd have to chew to hold me over until then.

I was so hyperaware of my body that I started body checking: looking at my body in every mirror I passed. I would engage in weird body rituals, like sitting on the floor and wrapping my hands around my thighs to see if my fingers would touch. I would run my hand down my back and see if I could feel my ribs. With all this chaos going on in my body, it didn't take long before I lost my period, completely.

As much as I told myself that I couldn't understand why I wasn't getting a normal period, I knew exactly why. Our body needs energy to maintain life. Our cycle prepares us to sustain a pregnancy. If we are barely keeping ourselves alive, it's going to shut down the system that's needed to keep another human alive. *Cue the "Put your mask on first" airplane safety video.* My mask was *not* on, and my plane was slowly crashing.

I went to several gynecologists who all echoed, "We're not sure why you aren't getting a regular cycle. You're young so let's put you on birth control to get you bleeding again."

I didn't want to be on birth control. Being on birth control never made sense to me...or my mom. I wasn't having sex. I wanted something that would help my body work naturally, not just cover up the problem.

Out of all the gynecologists I went to, there was only one who sat me down in her office and said, "You know, sometimes when women don't eat enough and lose weight, their body stops menstruating."

I side-eyed her, annoyed, because I knew what she was saying was true. Though instead of agreeing with her, I said, "Well, that's not what this is. I'm eating just fine."

Damn, was I stubborn.

I mean, come on, that's *exactly* what was happening. I wasn't ready to admit it, much less start eating more. I needed her to come up with another explanation or figure out a different solution.

I only got my period three to four times within seven years, not counting the fake period bleeds from the few times I did try birth control, which were always short-lived. My body may have been confused, but my intuition was still trying to send me small messages. I could hear it whisper into my soul, *"Birth control is not what you need."*

The few times I got my period were the happiest days of my life. I would go to the restroom, see blood, and scream out, "THANK YOU, GOD!" I'd walk out with a spring in my step and a smile from ear to ear as if I'd just won a new car. I'd call my mom and my sister, tell all my friends, and even share it with women who happened to be in the restroom with me.

I felt unstoppable! My body was finally doing what it needed to do, and it made me feel so normal, a feeling I didn't often get. I felt like my body was softly whispering, "Lucia, we got this. There's still hope." Each time I would see blood, I felt at ease. It was a sweet reminder that my body was working.

It's interesting that having my body work the way it was "intended to" made me feel like I could finally fit in. I felt like if I could have my body menstruate, then it meant I was doing things right as a woman. I was fulfilling the one simple thing that I believed was a side effect of being an adult woman. I was, however, less alone in this than I thought. I learned later in life that cycle irregularities are pretty common, especially among women with disordered eating and eating disorders. Our bodies are constantly trying to take care of us and won't allow more than what we can handle. It wasn't until years later, when I was deep into healing my relationship with food and exercise, that my cycle came back.

Chapter 4

Depths

My body was starved and confused. So was I.

During these ten years of struggle, I disconnected from my body's ability to communicate with me. It might have been trying to communicate, but I would only hear it when the communication became so loud – aka HANGRINESS, BINGES, and INTENSE desires to eat – that I couldn't physically ignore it.

Not only was my mind now consumed with food thoughts and ways to make itself smaller, but also it was robbing me of my ability to focus on my life.

I would turn down social outings **all** the time, so much so that I was always alone. I had so much fear about eating out, eating in front of others, or eating foods that I wasn't comfortable eating that I always found excuses as to why I couldn't join in. Not only was I good at finding excuses, but I was also really good at keeping myself busy. If I was busy, then *I* was in control. I was the one to choose whether something fit into my day or not, whether it was people, food, or gatherings. *Sorry I can't, I have to work. I have an exam coming up. I'm working to save money. I have to be up early tomorrow. I already have plans. I don't like that type of food. I gave up sweets for Lent.*

The list went on and on. There was always an excuse. I was stuck in a vicious cycle. I'd turn down almost every invitation to go out because I was worried about not having control over what I ate, yet I would end up alone at home eating an unsatisfying, low-calorie meal only to end up devouring a ton of "healthy snacks" afterward. I hated each time it would happen and every single time I would ask myself what would've happened if I'd just gone out and enjoyed a nice meal with my friends instead. *Why couldn't I join in like everyone else?* The truth is, I didn't know how to break the cycle. Deep in my disorder, the simplest choices were the hardest ones to make. My eating disorder wouldn't allow it. Anytime I considered choosing something I wanted, the disordered voice would kick in with all its lies, "You're going to gain weight. You'll end up eating a ton of food and you're going to feel guilty afterward." The voice left me feeling hopeless and weak, wondering why I couldn't get myself to stop or "to do better."

The rare times I did go out, I'd only ever order a salad or grilled chicken and vegetables. Now, there's nothing wrong with those options, but for me, I had no choice in it. I had lost my freedom to choose. The disorder was always choosing for me and every time it did, I was left more and more unsatisfied. When we are no longer in choice, our choices are no longer healthy, even when the choice is deemed "healthy" by society.

The few times I did attend social events, I only allowed myself to attend after I'd exercised enough and made sure not to eat too much before attending. I told myself that if I had control over everything up until the event, then I'd be okay with eating what was there. That was never how it turned out. I'd show up, be in my head the entire time, miss out on connection, barely eat what was there or feel guilty about what I had eaten, then arrive back home, still hungry, and end up having to eat something else. My entire brain space was consumed with food thoughts from the time I woke up to the time I went to bed. I was a slave to my mind.

As much as I wish I would've come to terms with my eating disorder and my need for help earlier in life, God presented it to me when I was ready. Not ready to dive in, but ready to release some control. Shortly before getting help, I started turning to Him more and more to ask for guidance in my life rather than asking for what I thought I needed. The times I asked

Him to guide me, it never failed. It was always scary to sit in silence waiting for the exact answer I knew I needed to hear. In fact, it was terrifying, though something in me was ready to hear it and ready for a change. I wanted my life back.

Chapter 5

Divine Timing and Gifted Challenges

After working my butt off my freshman year of college, I reapplied to A&M and was accepted. God continued to guide me. In my first semester at A&M, the roommate I matched with was also a nutrition major whose roommate before me had just taken a break from school to pursue healing from her eating disorder. Little did I know that I was matched with the person who would soon give me a glimpse into my healing journey.

At the time, I was deep into my eating disorder: I was barely eating and running off fumes. My body was so used to running on empty that having energy was a very foreign feeling. It still makes me cringe to think how little I was eating. It's a miracle I made it through. I know not everyone is that fortunate.

Late one evening, after I had barely eaten – and yet had convinced myself I had – I was lying on the top bunk of my metal-framed bunk bed. I was depleted and exhausted. I was ready to fall asleep right when my roommate walked in. She was surprised I was already in bed since it wasn't that late. As she entered the room, I got a hint of that warm, delicious peanut-oil fried chicken smell. I looked over at her and saw she was holding a perfectly wrapped, silver foil-covered, Chick-fil-A sandwich.

"Hey....I just went to Chick-fil-A and we got an extra chicken sandwich. I already ate mine. Do you want it?"

I bolted up.

My eyes widened, "You *really* don't want it?!"

"Nope, I already ate one."

I *never* allowed myself to eat Chick-fil-A or any other fun food. It was fast food. It was fried chicken. It was all the things I told myself I shouldn't eat because of all the stupid food rules that had been cemented into my brain.

Though, you better believe, I *loved* Chick-fil-A. I quickly slid down the side of my bunk bed and sat at my desk to eat it. I opened up the packaging and took my first bite.

Wow.

How could food taste **this good?** It only took a few more bites before it was gone. I got a little sad that such a joyful experience lasted only a few moments. I was left wanting more, yet I had no idea when I'd allow myself to eat something so satisfying again.

I was so underweight and undernourished that savoring a fried chicken sandwich on warm bread made my soul soften and my heart fill with joy. I hadn't experienced the joyful, warm, tingly feeling of savoring a meal in years. The feeling that makes you want to shimmy and shake your shoulders as you bob your head with a dorky smile across your face. ***Pure food bliss***.

I couldn't remember the last time I had been excited about eating something. The crunchy outside and warm inside of that chicken sandwich were heavenly. I could taste the distinct flavor of the peanut oil it was cooked in and the small, powerful hint of those two crunchy pickles perfectly positioned between the bread and the chicken. It was glorious.

That brief moment of food joy was a small glimpse into what I would later experience in my healing journey with food; I'd find satisfaction and comfort again. I don't know if it was from the excitement I felt or the fact that I had given my body delicious, satisfying calories, but I suddenly got a rush of energy. I might as well have just had sixteen ounces of strong coffee.

I got **chatty**, real quick. I was wide awake. I hadn't had that much energy in who knows how long.

Was this what it was like to have energy, to feel happy and satisfied after a meal? Is this what other people were experiencing when they ate?

I know my experience was heightened because my body had been restricted for so long, but in that moment, all I could think about was how good I felt.

I know God gifted me with my roommate and that specific moment as a small glimpse into what recovery would look like. No, not *every* meal experience was like that, but discovering foods again that I enjoyed was such an awakening experience. It's no coincidence that years later, the food that helped me discover satisfaction again was Chick-fil-A. Things always come full circle. Everything, even brief experiences, has its place in our life.

Part of intuitive eating, in my experience, is trusting that just like each person is put on our path for a reason, each food and eating experience is too. God has a way of challenging us when He knows we're ready for it. When we're ready and especially when we don't think we are yet, God will present us with the exact food challenge we need. It might come through a family event, a road trip, a fun date, or dinner at our in-laws. It's all planned out, perfectly crafted just for us.

This is something that has continued to help me through my always-changing and forward-moving relationship with food: knowing that whatever is available to me, food or otherwise, it's there for a reason. God is always supporting me in my journey, even and especially, when it feels extremely challenging and annoying.

Chapter 6

"I Want Your Abs"

My eating disorder brought me to love physical activity to the extent that it became a regimented part of my life. I lived in my head thinking about how much I worked out, when my next workout would be, and what foods I would eat in between. Even though I felt like a slave to physical activity, I didn't care to question it because our society does such a good job of normalizing it. *Oh, you made it to a workout class? Well, Mary Jane over here just finished two and is planning on taking yoga later. Oh, you want to take a day off? Well, Eddie over there ran X miles this morning before 8am.*

There was always someone doing more which made me justify that what I was doing was nothing abnormal. Yup, nothing to look at over here.

HA! Yeah right.

One of the realizations I had during my healing journey was that all of my friend circles included physical activity. I couldn't get away from it. I was surrounded by people moving their bodies and talking about health. It was one of my favorite ways of socializing.

For those trying to heal their relationship with food and their body, being surrounded by others who are constantly physically active makes it even more challenging to pull away from, or even figure out, what's healthy and normal.

Not only was I surrounded by 40-day yoga challenges and sweat dates, but I also was heavily praised for my body. The times I got the most body compliments in my life were the times I was the most unhealthy and undernourished, but how would they have known?

"Ugh, can I just have your abs?"

I so badly wanted to say "please stop saying that. You have no idea what it's like to be me right now. You don't want this."

I can count on one hand the number of times I was fully able to disconnect from my racing and rigid mind to finally find flow and ease in my body. As much as physical activity brought me a lot of unease, it also gave me access to a peace I hadn't been able to feel before. It removed the stress, anxiety, and constant worry I had in my brain and finally gave me a moment of inner stillness and space.

I would find peace when I was midrun, past the first few dreadful miles where my legs felt heavy and sore. All of a sudden, my muscles would warm up, my mind would soften, and I would notice the temperature of the air on my skin. The world would suddenly slow down, or at least my experience of it had. I looked up and noticed the different shades of green on the leaves above me, the light of the sun reflecting off the buildings, cars, and people's faces. It was as if we were all softly glistening.

I felt free. Calm. Present to the world around me as if I were easefully just living, light and grounded on my two feet.

These were the small moments when I would pause and appreciate the life within me and appreciate not only the ability to move and change within myself, but also appreciate the lives of the people around me. I distinctly remember passing couples holding hands. I would pause and wonder if I'd ever be able to slow down and feel safe enough in my skin to have someone there with me. I would see fathers chasing their kids, laughing and screaming. *Would I ever have a family and kids to play with? Would I ever be able to get out of this disordered relationship with food, my body, and myself so that I could live and dedicate my time to more than controlling my body?* It was moments like these that God would show me the desires of my heart. I wanted nothing more than to be in connection with others, but my thoughts were getting in my way.

My eating disorder also brought me to yoga. I was in college, trying to figure out what my kinesiology elective would be. I didn't have healthy ways of dealing with stress in college. The only thing I knew to do was to be physically active and control my eating, which in turn was causing more stress. When I saw that yoga was an option, I immediately signed up for it. I figured everyone who practiced yoga was "in shape" so it would be the "perfect thing" to add in.

My first yoga teacher, coincidentally, shared how she had experienced her healing journey with food and her body. Yoga had taught her to care for her body in a new way. The day she shared that story, my heart skipped a beat. I instantly felt connected to her. She had a radiant glow about her that made me even more curious and excited about this new practice I had just found. After that class, something in me yearned to learn more about the practice. I bought an MTV yoga DVD (*yes, that was a thing back then*) because, at the time, that's where my teacher recommended I start. Every once in a while, I would put on my yoga DVD and practice in my parent's living room during summer and winter breaks.

My relationship with yoga has been one heck of a roller coaster ride. A year after graduating from my dietetic internship to become a dietitian, I found yoga again. At that time, I had picked up running as my new favorite hobby. I hadn't practiced yoga since college, but somehow, agreed to attend a hot yoga class with my older brother. He was working at Lululemon at the time and was always in the know about the hottest, best new studios and workouts to try. On my day off, he called me and asked me to join him.

Wait, wait….me?! You want to hang out with me?

I always thought my older brother was too cool for me so the thought of him wanting to spend time with me made my heart so happy. I got off the phone with him, shocked that I had just agreed to attend a **heated** yoga class. What was I thinking?

"What do I wear?" Wait...I need a towel? What happens if I pass out? Should I drink a ton of water before class? Am I stuck in there until it ends?" I was freaked out. I called him three more times just to be sure I had everything I needed.

I pulled up to an unevenly paved parking lot with signs everywhere saying I'd get towed.

Great. This was exactly what I needed before walking into a hot yoga class I wasn't even sure I'd live through. Perfect.

My brother walked over, hugged me, and handed me a mat. Seconds later, we were walking into an older building that smelled of incense and moist heat. As we walked into the quiet lobby, we were greeted by a young, greying man. He welcomed us, and I signed my life away.

As soon as we walked into the heated room, I realized the temperature wasn't as hot as I was expecting. It felt like another hot, humid Houston day, *except we were indoors.*

Everyone in the room was either wearing tight clothes or hardly any clothes at all. There I was wearing black shorts and a tank top that slid up my body each time I was in Down Dog. *Did anyone else feel this uncomfortable? Was I the only first-timer?*

We set up on the second row and class started. I remember the teacher calling out different body parts and movements. No one had ever put me in an inverted V shape and asked me to raise a leg, bend a knee, and open my hip before. This was for sure very different from what my yoga experiences had been like in college. It was fast, heated, sweaty, and pretty intimidating. As if that weren't enough, it felt like everyone else in the room were in sync and knew exactly what poses we were doing next. I, on the other hand, was like a rigid yet loose noodle flopping body parts left and right. At one point, the teacher came over to help me which made me even more uncomfortable.

*Was I **that** bad?*

I did not "connect to my body" during that class, but what I did know is that something shifted inside me. As we walked out, dripping sweat, I remember looking up at the sky and feeling clear. The world around me felt slower. The colors were more vibrant. I didn't have a single worry or anxious thought. *What had just happened?* I didn't know it then, but that experience was the beginning of my life-changing yoga transformation. Even though I got a brief glimpse of feeling anxiety-free, as soon as we walked over to Whole Foods to get juice, my busy mind kicked back in. *I couldn't drink juice...I hadn't accounted for drinking those calories that day.* Just like that, my eating disorder had ruined another opportunity for connection.

When we are in our heads, we miss out on connection. The people around us don't understand why we aren't present, they just know we aren't.

After that day, I signed up for a new student special and continued attending yoga classes. I wanted to feel that sense of ease again. One evening during class, while in Butterfly Pose, the instructor asked us to put our hands on our chests and feel the life within us. I had never stopped to listen to the sound of my breath or to feel the rise and fall of my belly as I breathed. Something deeper shifted. I felt energy within me. I felt God within my bones. It suddenly hit me how my body was full of life radiating through me and how caring for my body was helping care for the life within me.

At that moment, I wanted more for myself. I wanted a different experience in my body. I wanted to feel kindness and ease. I wanted to start treating and seeing my body in a new light.

Chapter 7

Healing Takes Work

My journey back into my body was slow and included more ups and downs than I realized. I would compare myself to other women and always feel like I fell short. *How did they do it? How did they look healthy and strong, have a fun and fulfilling job, be in a romantic relationship with a hot boyfriend,* **and** *not struggle with food and their body?!??!*

I didn't get it. *What was I missing? Was I as un-put together as I felt?* I would see pictures of women eating out with friends, sharing pasta, having drinks, or eating avocado toast in the morning, and I'd think to myself, *"Why can't I have that? Why can't I just eat normal foods and get to share meals with friends?"* I used to get angry when I'd scroll through Instagram and see someone eating a variety of foods.

She's lying. There's no way she eats all of that.

I couldn't fathom someone being able to eat normally. There had to be something she wasn't saying. The truth was, I was so frustrated because I never saw myself being able to do the same. How did people eat donuts and pizza and pasta and cookies and go out to eat and *enjoy* their food?! **How were they doing that and why couldn't I?!**

I had so many questions and emotions about everything: what I ate, what other people ate, what my body looked like and felt like, what other people's bodies looked like. It was *so* much. My brain was always full.

I finally had enough. I was tired of being exhausted, both mentally and physically. I was tired of thinking about food, exercise, and my body. I wanted more for my life. That's when I knew I needed a change. Picking up the phone and calling another dietitian, while being a dietitian, and saying that I was ready to get help was the boldest thing I've ever done. Every muscle in my body relaxed as I physically felt a huge weight lift off of my shoulders. A life shift was about to happen; I was choosing to let go of the life I had been living.

I could feel the fire inside me as I dialed my dietitian's phone number. I called in the middle of my workday. I sat at the edge of my rigid, grey office chair softly looking out to a beautiful and bright sunny day glistening off the Medical Center skyline. I patiently waited for her to pick up. Even though it was terrifying, my body felt calm. I felt at home, strong in my skin, as if nothing could knock me out of my chair even if it wanted to. Her voicemail came on, and before I could overthink leaving a message, I was speaking. "Hi!!! My name is Lucia. I'm a dietitian and I'm pretty sure I have an eating disorder. I'm ready to get help. My friend recommended you to me. Please call me back when you get a chance. I can't wait to start working with you."

Mic drop.

I was ready. I was so confident and ready to admit to those who knew me that I needed support. *I'm here, world, and I need help.* There was nothing more freeing than feeling ready to be seen.

When our body knows, *it knows,* and it shifts us into action. As soon as we make a decision that will shift our life forever, we feel it. All of our senses awaken. It's that sweet whisper *saying, you're on the right track.* It's moments like this that our body stores forever.

I still remember the first day of nutrition counseling. I took the day off work because I wanted to have as much space and peace as I needed before taking that first step. My disordered brain told me to go to the gym and work off the stress, partly because it would help me ease some nervous energy before going into my first session and partly because I knew that the weight she would get that day would be my starting point. I thought to myself, the thinner I was starting, the thinner I would be coming out of it. *These were the kind of illogical, distorted thoughts I had racing through my head.*

Ironically, that's not how recovery works. I would soon learn all about set-point weight theory and how smart our body was made to be. Our body was designed to favor a certain weight range. It's the range that supports our body and mind to work the way it was intended. It's the range that allows us to focus *less on food and more on life.* If you would've explained that to me back then, I would've rolled my eyes. But sometimes, that's necessary. We have to go through denial and annoyance to get to the truth. Those eye rolls were needed, even if just for myself.

The first session I had with my dietitian was really easy. I felt comfortable and opened up about my entire history with eating and my body. It was the first time I shared *everything* from how and when it started to each traumatic moment that contributed to my journey with my current struggles. For the first time in a long time, I felt like myself. I was seen and heard, and there I was, *still standing.*

Sometimes getting the words out is the energetic release we need, releasing years of thoughts and emotions that were deeply and tightly bottled up suffocating and isolating us into more disorder. My heart felt softer. I had taken the first step, and ironically, I felt lighter. The more we share our thoughts with others, the more we're able to neutralize them. Getting them out of our body takes away their power.

It took years and a lot of guidance from God to get me to this first step in healing.

I'm not going to lie and say that healing is easy, because it's not. It's also not linear. There were wins and there were days where I felt like the world was sinking and I was drowning. That's why I was so grateful to have support.

My sessions were challenging. I would laugh, cry, get angry, and feel unbelievably annoyed at myself, my dietitian, and the world. I felt like everything I once thought I knew was being challenged. My eating disorder had served a purpose. It was helping me manage stress and anxiety. It was helping me feel safe, even though my body felt anything *but* safe.

I had made myself believe that if I focused on food and my body, I wouldn't have to deal with other uncomfortable things. I wouldn't have to feel as much because I was numbing all my emotions. My eating disorder was good at tricking me into feeling like everyone was plotting against me *all* of the time. I was reactive to most people and most things. Later, I came to realize that I felt this way because I didn't feel safe in my skin. My body was doing what it knew to do to defend itself.

When I think back to myself sitting in sessions, I see myself sitting rigidly with stiff shoulders and arms and legs crossed, staring blankly at my dietitian. I was stubborn. Well technically, the eating disorder was.

God bless my dietitian for holding space and staying calm the whole time. She was always patient and guided me to uncover and unlearn exactly what I needed. I would never have been able to get to where I am today if it weren't for her.

One of the greatest gifts I got from our sessions was empathy toward others. I got to see firsthand how difficult it was to challenge my habits and beliefs around food. For the first time, in years of being a dietitian, I finally understood how my patients felt and how their families felt. I experienced how easy it can be to want something yet how hard it can be to choose it. Meeting with my dietitian changed my way of connecting and counseling with clients forever. I learned that *listening* is the most powerful thing we can do. Holding space for another human so they feel seen and heard is sometimes all they need. There were several days when that was all I needed – to be heard, to be validated for everything I was feeling and experiencing, and to be told that it was okay. I came to realize that the best sessions were the ones where I could freely verbalize the hot mess that was in my head while my dietitian politely listened. Our brain is good at routines and old habits, so naturally, anything that challenges them is a threat. Not once was I judged, but I was *always* challenged, and for that, I am forever grateful. The empathy I gained showed up in my sessions with clients. I no longer got annoyed if a patient of mine didn't do what I had suggested. Instead, I got curious as to why and how I could continue to support them moving forward. I learned that it was okay to take a few steps back and not be where I wanted to be. It wasn't going to happen in my self-created timeframe. Almost nothing does. It happens in God's time. That's the raw beauty and messiness of healing. It happens just as it needs to, with crazy challenges along the way.

There was always a way to keep moving forward, even if it meant *feeling more versus doing more*. We can't change our relationship with food by continuing to do the same things that got us to an unhealthy place. Recovery took doing the opposite, and many times, it meant not doing much of anything at all. To create a new life, I had to create new ways of being and new values to live my life by. I had to start creating the future I wanted.

Chapter 8

Divinely Guided

I didn't understand intuition or how powerful it would be in my life until I found intuitive eating. Until then, my intuition was not something I ever thought about. I could always tell when I was doing something I wasn't supposed to be doing because my body felt off, but I never paid much attention to it. I had never thought about how incredible our body sensations are and how each one of them has a distinct purpose in our life. Body sensations are how our body communicates with us. God created our body and gave each body sensation a purpose. When we listen to our body and honor what it is communicating with us, we are working *with* the body God designed instead of against it. Our intuition guides our body's natural flow. But I neither understood nor acknowledged this back then.

I was fourteen years old when I first felt God – truly felt God and my intuition in a way that my whole body suddenly felt like I was floating through space. My eyes were closed. The only light I sensed was the bright light coming from the stage where my youth minister stood playing his guitar, singing praise and worship. The room was packed with high school kids, but at that moment, it was me and God. Even in that cold room, I felt the inner warmth of my body, the kind where my heart felt full and every muscle in my body was at ease. The kind where all I could think about was the words I was singing. The kind where my eyes suddenly filled with tears of joy.

It's moments like this I'll never forget. Moments where I feel God's presence in my body and my heart. The more open I am to receiving these moments, the more often I notice them happening in my life. For me, it has been more about acknowledging, feeling, and taking the time to listen to them. God not only lives within all of us, but He also is constantly communicating with us. He is always whispering into our souls and listening for the deepest desires of our hearts. He knows what we need and provides it to us when it's time.

A few months into my healing journey, I sat cross-legged across from my dietitian and questioned everything she was saying about "trusting my hunger" and how my body "always knows exactly what it needs."

Haha...ummm, yeah right. That's cute.

I was annoyed and skeptical. She leaned closer to me, "Lucia, do you ever question your need to pee or that you've peed just the right amount?"

"...No," I answered as I crossed my arms.

"Do you ever get nervous that you took in too much air or didn't breathe enough out?"

"...Nope."

I was starting to see where she was going with this.

"Why not?" she asked with a curious smile.

"Because my body knows how much and how often to do those things."

"Exactly. Do you *really* think God got all your other organ systems right and just messed up the digestive one?"

Ugh, don't you hate when they're right? I was mind blown and speechless.

These were the moments when I got to think about food and hunger in a new way. New pathways of thinking and being were slowly being carved out for me. Hunger and fullness weren't something to be feared or questioned, they were made to keep me alive. It suddenly hit me. *Every part of my body was working to keep me balanced.* Connecting it all back to how and why I was created allowed me to start having faith in my own body and to trust the process. God knew what He was doing when He breathed life into me. It was me that was lacking faith in myself and in Him.

Intuitive eating was the first way of understanding nutrition that truly resonated with my beliefs. The concepts weren't trying to get me to conform to another diet. They were concepts that left me feeling curious about how to listen better and attune to the body I was given instead of trying to fit my body into a mold that wasn't mine.

Hearing, appreciating, and trusting my body sensations didn't come easily for me. Learning to trust what I was feeling and hearing was, and *still is,* one of the most challenging things for me. Why? Because my mind takes over. It takes time to let go of all the crazy food and body ideals that we've been sold for so long. But, when we finally choose to listen, it's the most freeing feeling, even if the journey there is challenging.

Each time I tried to control my body and my life, I found myself disconnected from God and my purpose in life. I thought I was living a God-centered life, however, my priorities and values didn't reflect it. My disordered eating pushed me further away from my body and my faith. Trusting my body wasn't even an option. I was so focused on my body, yet all of my focus was on *controlling* my body, not listening to it.

It wasn't until I was in the messiness of my healing journey that I learned how to start giving up control. Having food and my body as my idols wasn't giving me the life I wanted; it was creating a life barely lived.

We can't heal until we give up the need to control. We can only freely live when we've accepted that we have *no control.* Control is not what we need. Trust and faith are what guide us and keep us whole. The more I listened and asked for help, the more peace I felt in my heart and the more at ease I felt in my body. To heal, I needed not only to have faith in the process and God's plan but also in the body He created for me. All of that took work and a lot of patience.

Through my healing journey, I learned to sit with my emotions... and boy, were they **loud**. I had spent so much time running away from them and tuning them out that when I finally slowed down to listen, I was overwhelmed. How could I be feeling **this much**?!

How was I supposed to manage life, work, and relationships while giving myself time to feel all of it *and* keep moving forward? I wished *so badly* that I could put everything else on hold. Trying to manage all of it felt like a lot, and it wasn't graceful. I would sit in the middle of my living room floor, crying, asking myself when it would all stop.

Was it normal to be this emotional and feel so much? Would it ever stop?

It felt like my body was getting out all the emotions it had suppressed and pushed down *for years*. It was going to take time. Allowing myself to feel, communicated to my body that I was listening. I was present for it. I was connected. Once all the emotions settled, my body started communicating with me more often. My intuition woke up.

My intuition gives me peace in a world that is constantly moving. It's as if my stomach detaches from the rest of my body and sinks closer to my soul. The slight churning that happens is different from the churning that happens when I feel hungry. It's a tiny discomfort in the pit of my stomach that can't be ignored – an emptiness that lingers until I make the right decision, the decision my body knows it needs to make.

Now that I've felt it so many times, my intuition feels familiar and it has never failed me. **Not once** have I followed my gut and had it go sour. I can, however, think of plenty of times when I didn't listen and then wished I would have. My relationship with my changing body and my roller coaster of a relationship with food caused me to disconnect from my body because I no longer trusted it. It was doing things I didn't like, so why would I trust it?

Who gave you permission to change, body?

I hadn't.

It took experiencing severe discomfort in my body and complete disconnection to allow me to treasure what it feels like for my body to work with me symbiotically rather than feeling like I'm playing an aggressive game of tug of war. It is experiences like this that allow me to have faith. My inner knowing, my physical experiences of the world around me, and my body's ability to sense and respond just as it needs to, are a gift.

When I speak about intuition, I'm not speaking about some woo-woo idea. I'm speaking about God. He created me exactly the way He intended. Intuition is feeling that nauseating bitterness in my mouth when I'm doing something I know I shouldn't be doing versus the smoothness and ease in my body when I'm doing something that's meant for me.

These deep, physical, and inner-body sensations can't be ignored. They are our compass. They keep us on our path and in line with our purpose. Each person we meet, each conversation we have, and each action we take are on purpose and our body knows that.

When we learn to trust our intuition, we start hearing it more clearly. We start feeling and sensing those tiny subtle physical signals. What if we stopped waiting for our 20/20 hindsight vision to kick in and decided to trust the current moment we're in? What if we chose to be more present in what is happening?

Intuition isn't scheduled. It shows up whenever it wants to. I can be standing in the middle of the lotion aisle at Target and get a strong sense to call my mom, only to hear her say she was reaching for her phone to call

53

me. Or, how about the time I ignored my gut feeling when I felt something was off with my 1995 Chevy Malibu only to find myself 30 minutes later on the side of the road with an overheated car and blown gaskets. There are also the physical sensations I get every single time I meet someone new or run into someone I already know. My body knows when there's something wrong, when they're uncomfortable, or if there's something they aren't telling me. My body knows whom to trust. My intuition is always leading me, and if I hadn't listened, I would've never found healing.

It was a normal Tuesday, and I was sitting at my computer desk at work scrolling through my emails when an email from a Yoga Foundation caught my eye. I didn't even have to open it to know that what was in that email was important. I got a sudden sharp, twisty feeling in my gut. My body was intrigued. As soon as I opened it and read about the upcoming retreat, I knew I had to be there.

I had been wanting to attend that specific yoga training for over a year. I had graduated from my first yoga teacher training and was ready and eager to keep learning. Taking that training made sense since most of the teachers at my studio had already attended. Each time someone would attend, they would come back a different person, a stronger teacher. They were confident and spoke words that resonated with my soul. My body wanted me to be at that retreat, but my mind was terrified to go. The thought of going on a week-long yoga retreat in the middle of nowhere where I wouldn't have access to my schedule and my routine, was terrifying. I did the thing I knew to do. I called a good friend, who was also "health-conscious" and had attended that same training the prior year.

"What do you think is holding you back from going?"

I paused. Not because I didn't know, but because my answer made me realize how enslaved I was to my own life.

"...I...um...I'm honestly just nervous about not being able to work out the way I do and have my normal eating routine and foods. For *some reason* (but I knew exactly why), it makes me uncomfortable."

"Lucia...it's a YOGA retreat. You are going to be doing a lot of yoga every day and they serve you a vegetarian diet. Girl, you'll be fine."

And then she spoke the words I needed to hear: "Maybe if you're so scared of going, it's exactly why you should go."

She was right.

It might sound silly, but at that time, not having the ability to control and know exactly what I would be eating and how long I'd be physically active for was **terrifying**. Terrifying to the point where I could feel my body tense up and my gut feel queasy and empty.

For the past ten years, I'd been in complete control over how much I ate and how much I moved. I didn't travel. I didn't socialize much. My eating disorder had kept me from all of it: venturing out, traveling, and trying new things. It kept my life small. There was now a fire burning inside me. I was ready for fear to stop holding me back, and I was tired of my obsession with control holding me back in my life.

As soon as we got off the phone, I got a strong urge to head to adoration, a silent Catholic devotional tradition of spending time with the consecrated Eucharist. I rarely went to adoration, but that evening something in me knew I had to go.

It was late in the evening, and the parking lot was nearly empty. I parked and walked over to the older, more intimate chapel. As quietly as I could, I opened the door and immediately felt a sense of ease enter my body. The room was lit by the gleaming light of small, red candles burning on the sides of the room. The smell of incense immediately greeted me as I entered. I looked over at the Eucharist, held within a large, beautiful golden monstrance, and made my way over to an old wooden chair with green upholstery. I got down on one knee, made the sign of the cross, and sat down. There's nothing like the silence that was in that room.

Without fail, like every other time I'd sat alone in this chapel, it only took a few minutes until tears started flowing down my cheeks. I couldn't explain it, but I felt moved and connected to God's presence, not only in the room but also within my own body. I sat there in silence, palms open, ready to receive whatever it was God wanted me to hear.

I cried and cried, not understanding why. Amid my tears, I felt as if someone had whispered into my soul: *Lucia, you have to go. You need to be there.*

That was all it took. The next day, I picked up the phone and called the retreat coordinator.

"Look, I know the retreat is in two weeks and I have no idea how I'll get there, but I know I need to be there."

Even though I couldn't see her face, I felt it. The lightness. Her bright, warm smile as soon as I spoke those words. "Well, it sounds like you're meant to come, how can I support you in getting here?"

And just like that, I decided I was going.

This was so unlike me. I wasn't someone who randomly took days off from work for a fun event. I was someone who had saved up enough vacation time to cover maternity leave (and I wasn't even close to being married, much less having a child). I liked lists and plans and structure. I still remember calling my manager thinking *surely, she won't let me take a full week off work with such short notice.*

"Sure, Lucia, as long as one of the other two outpatient dietitians aren't off that week, it's all yours."

Wait, what? That was easy.

It's crazy how as soon as you make a decision that feels right within your soul, everything falls into place...and I mean *everything*.

I got a last-minute flight to New York, figured out how to get from the crazy airport to a busy bus station, found a specific bus that would take me to the middle of nowhere, where another car – with someone I also didn't know – picked me up and would supposedly get me to the retreat center I had only just heard about. I was a tad overwhelmed. Not to mention the fact that for the whole hour and a half ride on the bus, I would have zero cell phone reception.

Apparently, when I jump into discomfort, I go all in. That's faith. It's choosing what you know is right even when your logical brain thinks you're insane and your parents look at you like you're crazy. In my heart, I knew something big would happen at that retreat. Something that would shift everything. Little did I know, it would be the start of my healing journey.

I wouldn't be where I am today had I not been okay with the discomfort of doing something new for the sake of following my heart. This retreat changed my life. It introduced me to the exact person I needed to connect with, someone who had found healing in her journey with food and her body just a few years prior.

It was the second to the last day of the retreat, and I was participating in an exercise they had us do where half the room would scream while pushing against another person, as the person being pushed would resist. Our role was to scream out whatever we wanted to give up or get out.

I started yelling.

As soon as I did, I started crying.

*"I'm tired. I am **so tired**. I don't want to do this anymore..."*

More tears.

"I don't want to live this way. I'm tired of feeling stuck. I'm tired of having to work out all the time. I'm tired of not enjoying food. I'm tired of hating my body. I'M JUST SO TIRED. I don't want this anymore. I don't *[tears]*...want *[sniffles]*...*THIS*...*[more tears]* anymore!"

I was shocked but also relieved that the words had finally come out of my mouth.

I had been waiting to say those words for **years**...and just like that, it was out. At that very moment, something changed within me. *What had just happened?* That night as I fell asleep, I felt empty, and also very numb. I wasn't sure what would come out of this but I could feel something was brewing. The next morning was our last morning at the retreat. I was sitting at the breakfast table with the two friends I'd made during the week, one being the one who'd gone through her own healing journey. Right there, while eating fruit and oatmeal, I felt the need to be honest with her. I told her about my eating disorder.

She kindly looked me right in the eyes and said, "I knew you were struggling from the moment I met you. I could see it in your face. I could see it in your eyes. There was so much sadness and suffering within them."

We both started crying. She went on to tell me about her healing journey and what it was like to go through counseling. For the first time in my life, I wanted nothing more than to heal.

When God knows we're ready, it starts unfolding.

That, my friends, is proof that God is always leading us. He places the people we need the most at the right place at exactly the right time. Who would have thought that traveling to a small town in New York would have led me to meet just the person I needed to before my journey began back in Houston. There's no denying that every little thing happens for a reason. Our body doesn't lie. Our intuition is always working in our favor, even when we don't yet see it. That to me is nothing short of a miracle. That to me is divine guidance. What you need will find you in the most unexpected time and place, but it will find you. It's your choice to be open to seeing it and open to choosing it.

Other than guiding me on my path to healing, my intuition led me to leave unhealthy relationships and start new ones, leave a super stable job, jump into uncertainty, move apartments, and have faith in making scary money decisions that provide me with no real certainty. If I've learned anything from letting go and allowing myself to be guided, it's this: the more we hold on, the more stuck and lost we feel. The more we allow ourselves to be guided, the more easily our journey unfolds.

What does it take to harness strong faith, a powerful intuition, and the bravery to pursue them? Leaning into what we sense, even when it's challenging.

Chapter 9

Welcoming Anxiety

After meeting with my dietitian for a few months, I had learned a lot about myself and my relationship with food. But what I also learned was that so much of my funky relationship with food and my body had very little to do with food and my body. It had a lot to do with everything else. It had a lot to do with my anxiety. Up until then, I had *no idea* I even had anxiety.

My normal state of being was one of frustration and annoyance. While driving, I'd curse at one car after another, and zoom my little red Toyota Corolla in and out of traffic. My body and mind were jumpy. I always felt ruffled energy crawling through my skin.

I was annoyed by *every little thing.* Every light. Car. Song on the radio. Train. Random person driving slowly. Any person speeding. Pretty much everyone.

I was over it.

Everyone was in my way and *how dare they*?!

Rage.

I couldn't control it. It lived within me and would often show its ugly face without any warning.

It didn't just show up on my drives through the city. It showed up as I got ready for work in the morning, when my mom would try to have a conversation with me after work, or when something unplanned or unexpected happened.

Basically...it happened *a lot.*

I lived in a state of annoyance. I was annoyed that dinner wasn't ready when I needed it to be. I was annoyed at simple questions people would ask me. I was quick to react and say things I didn't mean. I *hated* when I had a plan for what would be my *perfect* day and was asked to do something different that would disrupt it. Just like that, my day would go from being perfect to being a hot mess. If one thing was off, everything was off.

Why? Because I loved being in control. My plan meant safety and security and only *me* being in charge. I was a bit of a control freak. If I wasn't in control, I was annoyed and difficult to be around.

To this day, I can still feel the empty, nauseating feeling I would get each time my dad would ask, "Why are you *so* reactive? Why can't anyone ask you anything?" or when my mom would say "Que te pasa [what's wrong with you]" in that high-pitched, boss-lady tone only my mom had mastered.

I lived annoyed but had no idea why. When people would ask me why I was so reactive or why I was always so stressed, my soul would shrink inside. I so badly wished I knew why I was the way I was and more importantly, why no one else had this issue. It sucks not knowing why you're acting a certain way or why your body feels so off while constantly being asked if you have the answer. I definitely didn't. It wasn't until YEARS later that I began to understand the connection between my behavior, my disordered eating, and my anxiety.

One day, my dietitian politely asked, "Wouldn't it be great if your disordered eating were *just anxiety*?!"

Uuuhmmm...*just* anxiety? I was furious. *Me? Anxious?* Get outta town.

I had no idea I had anxiety. I mean, let's be real, the initial thought of being someone who has anxiety only made me *more anxious.*

Do you want to know what's even funnier? *I was the one making my anxiety worse.*

How?

Because I was dieting and underfeeding myself.

Dieting exacerbates anxiety and anxiety exacerbates dieting. Dieting is fueled by anxiety and anxiety is fueled by dieting. When you're hungry, or let's say, casually underfeeding yourself, your body can't stand it.

Your body wants food and energy *to live*.

Because I was undereating and placing so much attention on food, not only was I constantly "hangry," but my stressed body was in a constant state of fight or flight.

Well, I was for sure *fighting*. I was defensive. Quick to anger. Irritable. Not someone you wanted to hang out with. I was NOT the version of me that I now know to be me. It's almost impossible to live in a constant state of hunger and pretend like things won't piss you off or stress you out.

Our body is like, "Hello! **Feed me**. Pay attention to me! When's our next meal? Can it be now?" And we're like "Nah, I'm good. I got things to do."

If you starve yourself, your body rebels. And it's not pretty. Your body will do everything in its power to **get your attention**. And when you ignore it, it will make you irritable, cranky, and mean. Anxiety isn't just constant worry. Anxiety can look like irritability, restlessness, or feeling on edge. Why? Because in those moments, your body doesn't care about doing *anything else* other than surviving. Why would it? Its priority is to keep you alive.

Soon after I came to terms with the fact that I was experiencing anxiety,

I learned how intertwined and connected anxiety and eating disorders were. Again, I had no idea. That's why meal timing was such a big deal for me, and why not having my favorite foods around would turn an incredible day into the worst day ever, in a matter of seconds. My body was crying inside because it was so hungry and physically and emotionally stressed. No wonder I couldn't handle the daily stresses of life. I had reached my limit. I was the kind of person who would always take on more because I "could," only to find myself at work staring at my computer screen crying several times a month. It wasn't just work that undid me – it was everything. I never allowed myself to slow down, yet I could barely handle all the obligations I continued to take on.

It's no surprise that a delayed mealtime set me off. A delayed mealtime was like telling a starving, exhausted toddler he needs to wait another two hours to eat. Not a fun scenario. That was me. A hangry, low blood-sugar woman walking around trying to keep everything together...and it wasn't working.

I still remember the day I came to terms with the fact that I had anxiety and allowed my struggle to be real. I was driving home from my clinical dietitian job. I had no music on. The sun was glistening, shining through my untinted car window onto my cool skin. I felt at peace.

"What if it *is* just anxiety?" As soon as I allowed myself to entertain that thought, I felt a sense of stillness and calm move through my whole body. Every muscle relaxed as I let out a soft, open-mouth sigh.

As soon as I stopped resisting the thought, it all started to make sense. *I'm not an angry or reactive person all the time. That's not me. It's my anxiety taking over.* I started to see the value in counseling and the value of listening to what my dietitian was saying even though it challenged me to my core. Sometimes the toughest thing to wrap our heads around is the very thing that transforms our life.

When my anxiety shows up, I usually get this jittery feeling in my legs and stomach, a need to somehow escape where I am. It's a desire to energetically purge all my feelings and emotions out of my body because they feel so intense. I immediately look for a distraction to ease my energetically full body. All I want to do is run, move, or get out of my own skin. My mind starts racing and I can't focus on what's at hand. Instead, my mind goes straight into the future and runs through a billion different scenarios that aren't logical, or happening in the present moment. It feels like my mind is on a race track and I'm sitting on the sidelines trying to keep up.

The reality is that my anxiety is *one* way my body communicates with me and tries to keep me safe. Coming to terms with experiencing anxiety from time to time has not only helped me prevent it and notice it coming on but also has helped me disarm it.

Being aware of my anxiety – what it feels like, and when it's creeping in – has changed my life. I now get to manage my anxiety rather than let it manage me. Simply recognizing when it is present has helped me pause and remember that I get to be in choice about how I respond to it. The key to helping me manage anxiety is pausing and breathing, something yoga unintentionally taught me. The minute I acknowledge that I'm feeling overwhelmed or stressed, I pause. I turn off any music, close my computer, and slide my phone away to where I can't see it. In these moments, I don't need more; I need less. I need to be in my body, not in my head. I need to be breathing. Allowing myself to breathe in a way that's slow and loud enough to where I can hear it. This grounds me instantly. It might take a few breaths or a few minutes, but it always helps. It is *exactly* what I need to remind myself that I am safe and that I am right where I need to be.

In my own experience, there is always *something* that triggers my anxiety. In pausing to check in with myself, I can get present with what I'm feeling and what the root cause of it is – which oftentimes is something different than what I expect it to be. Maybe it's something that bothered me that I didn't take the time to acknowledge. Maybe it has been too long since I've last eaten. Maybe I'm overwhelmed by the expectations I've set on myself or a timeline I've committed to. Acknowledging that anxiety is present allows me to separate myself from it. I am not my anxiety, just like I am not my eating disorder.

Over the past four years, my ability to ground myself has become easier, but it still isn't necessarily easy in and of itself. The more I diversify my tools to ground myself, the more accessible it feels. Throughout the years, I've found that I usually need something different each time. Sometimes, it's taking a hot shower or praying. Other times it's stretching or being in a grounding yoga pose for five minutes while focusing on my breath. Then there are days when the only thing that helps is stepping outside or moving my body.

As soon as I ground, I feel better. I remind myself that there's no impending doom and that I am okay right where I am, right where God wants me to be.

Anytime our body feels out of control, different, or off, it's *communicating with us.*

It is our job to listen, to get curious about what's going on, and to notice what it is we're sensing.

Our body always knows best, even when it feels like it's out of whack. There's something to get in each tiny moment of disaster. A message to receive, right at that moment.

It felt so freeing to finally understand that my frustration wasn't me. My rude and irritable responses weren't me. All the energy boiling up inside of me was my body waving a huge, neon sign saying *I'm trying to keep you safe!*

If you take anything from this chapter, let it be this:

Eating enough food can change your life and calm your body. And, always listen to what others see in you, even if what they have to say irritates you. It can be life changing, even – and especially – when you don't agree. Others can see and sense things that we might not be able to, especially a trained professional. Know that if you are getting irritated, it's for a reason. Irritation is another sensation – like anxiety – that your body uses to get your attention. If it weren't important, it wouldn't irritate you.

The more I chose to listen and feel instead of react, the more I started understanding and appreciating my body. I might experience anxiety from time to time, some days more than others, but my anxiety has led me to understand and listen to my body way more than I ever would have.

Part of tuning in to our body is knowing that not everything we feel and sense will be pleasurable or fun, and that's okay. We have to be able to know what feels off to be able to stay safe, well, and on our path. We have to know what's wrong for us in order to know what's right.

So, in my opinion, as much as anxiety can be inconvenient at times, I choose to see it as a gift. Take that as you choose, but all I know is that if it weren't for my anxiety, my journey to understanding and healing my body wouldn't have been the same. Acknowledging, understanding, and learning to manage anxiety has, and will continue to be, a key piece of my story.

Chapter 10

Getting Uncomfortable

A year and a half into my healing journey with food, I had my biggest physical breakthrough. It came right after a surgery I had avoided having for years out of fear. One of the side effects of having an unhealthy relationship with my body and food is that not only did I not trust myself but also I lacked faith in everyone else. I didn't trust people, *especially with anything regarding my body.* I refused to admit that others could help me care for it or understand it better.

I had known about my ovarian cyst for at least ten years at this point. It was shortly after I had stopped getting my period and was having all the medical exams and tests done to understand why, that they finally found it.

I had gone into my OBGYN's office because of irregular cycles, which I now know were *not* due to my cyst. I was 15 or 16 at the time and wasn't sexually active. I was young and I didn't need someone sticking a metal prong up my body and scraping. Ummm, **no thank you.** It did not feel right to have a pap smear done at that time, and I was so grateful my mom stood up for me. She always taught me that if something didn't feel right, it probably wasn't. My doctors agreed and suggested we order a transabdominal ultrasound. Thank goodness for following our gut, otherwise, we would've never known about my massive cyst.

I remember that day pretty clearly. I walked into a small waiting area filled with chairs and two giant upside down jugs of water with stacks of paper cups beside them. I was surrounded by women of all ages. Some of them looked sad, others looked worried, others joyful. How crazy to think that we can all be in the same waiting area, waiting for completely different tests, and end up leaving with completely different results. The variability of the human body and what we all go through never ceases to amaze me.

I was instructed to sit and drink water. They needed my bladder to be full before doing the ultrasound so there I was, in the cold waiting room, forcing myself to drink room temperature water out of one of those small white paper cups that makes the water taste like sandy plastic.

I got to the point where I needed to pee. Not a little, but a lot. I went up to the receptionists and told them I was ready.

"Well, honey, you're going to have to wait. Your tech isn't here yet."

Ummm hello, you could've given me a heads up about that; my bladder is about to explode.

My anxiety slowly crept in.

I sat back down, frantic and shaking my foot up and down. I squeezed my thighs together trying to hold it in while dreaming of the moment I'd not have to feel so uncomfortable. I finally got to the point where I couldn't hold it any longer. I ran to the nearest restroom and peed.

And you know what happened next? I had to start all over again.

My parents who were waiting with me weren't amused...and, well, neither was I.

After what felt like an eternity of being cold and annoyed, I continued counting down the seconds until I could empty my bladder again. They finally called me back. Together, we walked down a long, white hallway full of exam rooms. Three-quarters of the way down the hallway, we turned right into a small, dark room. The only things inside were a blue patient exam table and a small desk covered with fancy ultrasound equipment.

Y'all, why are those rooms so cold? Don't they know being cold is even more uncomfortable...and then they ask you to take off your clothes and slip into a half-open thin robe WHILE you're trying to keep your bladder from bursting. Who thought this through?

I was told to lay down on the cold exam table and wait for the technician. I lay there glaring at the clock, impatiently watching the second hand move from one black tick line to the next.

My brain started up again. *What if when she presses on me, I pee on the table? Then what? That has to be common around here. Also, why does everything take forever when I have to pee?*

Finally, the technician walked in, super sweet and smiley, taking her time. She squirted what felt like a huge blob of that cold, slippery, ultrasound jelly on my belly and started running the probe over my middle and lower abdomen. It was uncomfortable to say the least. More like nails on a chalkboard where the chalkboard was my bladder and the nails were the cold, white probe.

Who enjoys this? No one. That's who.

To distract myself, I looked over at her and her screen as if *I* had any idea what she was looking at. Suddenly, the energy in the room changed and she got quiet. She was focused on something. She started marking off different sections and taking pictures. I asked, "Is everything okay?"

"I'm just taking a few pictures. Your doctor will be here in a few seconds."

Um, okay....

Oh look, I found something...but I can't tell you what it is...*who doesn't get anxiety from that?*

I lay there twiddling my thumbs in silence for what felt like the longest seven minutes of my life. As soon as she finished, I jumped up and ran to the restroom. Finally, some relief.

A whole ten minutes later, my parents and I met with the doctor to get the news. I had a cyst...a pretty big one, just sitting there on my right ovary.

They gave me two options. I could either have surgery or just play the waiting game, waiting for it to grow or waiting for it to burst. The good news was that they didn't think it was anything to be concerned about. The bad news was that it felt like I had a ticking time bomb that could explode any minute and take my ovary with it.

Not exactly comforting or something you just casually forget about.

Over the years, I had it checked periodically. It never grew and no matter how many doctors looked at it, the answer was always the same. The choice was mine. I could have it removed and have peace of mind or leave it where it was and hope nothing happened.

There were months when I would forget about it all together, but once I started practicing yoga, every time I did a deep twist, I would feel it. It was a tender and tingly sensation that ran down my lower right hip. It would give me chills just thinking about it. *What if one day I'm in the middle of practice and it just bursts? What if today is that day?*

I'd always remind myself not to overthink.

After a few years, I got really good at not thinking about it until I started dating my now ex. When I first told him about it, he was shocked. "I can't believe you've just left it in there this whole time."

Ummm, yeah, I don't want surgery. If it ain't broke, don't mess with it.

It wasn't until we started getting more serious that the concern turned into, "Well, what happens if it bursts or starts growing while you're pregnant?"

Ugh. Don't you hate it when other people make a really good point?

If you haven't already noticed, I was the queen of avoiding uncomfortable situations. This time though, the thought that one day this cyst could potentially cause a complication for me and my future child was *just* the motivation I needed. Again, divine timing.

If I wouldn't have dated my ex, who knows if I would've ever had it taken out. And, if I hadn't been over a year and a half into my healing journey with food, I would've never felt comfortable enough to pursue it. The fear at this point was not so much about the surgery itself, but more about the recovery period.

It just so happened that one of my friends had just finished his first year of residency in gynecology and knew just the right surgeon for me. "He's a genius in the surgical room."

It felt seamless. As soon as I needed someone in my life, God gave me the right person.

At my scheduled appointment, the doctor and I talked all about the ins and outs of the surgery as well as the recovery period. The plan was to have my cyst removed laparoscopically through my belly button allowing it to be a simple day surgery. It'd take a few hours and I'd likely be home that same evening. I wasn't scared as much about having surgery, I was scared about the recovery.

"You'll need to take a full six weeks off of exercise."

My body froze. Suddenly, all I could hear were the thoughts in my head. I looked at him with disbelief and said "Wait, what? *Six weeks*?!" Surely, I'd misunderstood. How could a ***one-day*** surgery put me out for six weeks? I wasn't even allowed to do yoga. *Was he insane?* As soon as he saw the look of fear in my pale, wide-eyed face, he lightly laughed, tilted his head, and said, "You'll be fine. A lot of my active patients have the same fear. You're young, and you'll recover quickly."

That's when it hit me, I was more afraid of not being able to exercise for six weeks than I was about having surgery. Despite all the improvements in my eating habits and my relationship with food, my brain still had a tight grip around how, when, and how much I moved my body. God was giving me, right then and there, the opportunity to work on the area of my healing journey that challenged me the most.

I went home and sat with my thoughts. Even though I was scared, I knew I was ready. I knew God was putting this in my life because *He* knew I was ready. I had thought about having this surgery for over ten years and it was finally time. I had prayed and prayed that God would help me find a way to pause exercise and here it was. God had lined it up for me and everything about it was easefully falling into place. He knew it was the only way it was going to happen.

Days later, I found myself crying at my dietitian's office. I was so scared about taking time off of exercise but knew that if I could get through this, it would be pivotal in my healing journey. Change was coming. Sometimes it takes a scary event to change a disordered way of being, and oftentimes, it takes praying and surrendering to God to give us the exact thing we need.

Something I've learned in my healing journey is that if we wait to do something once the fear is gone, we'll never do it. The fear never goes away, but courage and faith are the bulky, strong boxing gloves that help us push through anything.

Up until this point, I had tried cutting back on physical activity but couldn't. It had become such a defining part of me that I didn't know how to function without it. It was hard to come to terms with the fact that a healthy habit had become so unhealthy. It was challenging to choose to do less of something that made me feel so good, at least momentarily.

So many questions flooded my mind. *How would I manage stress and anxiety?*

Could I even eat all the same foods without moving as much? Would my body know what to do? Would I lose all control? I didn't have the answers, but I was ready to find out.

Before my surgery, I had successfully cut back on running and started trying new ways of moving my body. Coincidentally, the person I ran with every morning had just moved, and running alone in the early morning was not an option. My boyfriend and I started trying different forms of exercise together. We started swimming and going on walks together. I even took a few dance classes at our local YMCA which was far outside my comfort zone.

I started seeing the benefits of trying different forms of movement, different intensities, and moving my body in ways that were fun. I got to experience how physical activity didn't have to be rigid or a form of punishment, unlike the messages I'd always heard from society.

Burn off that turkey. Earn your food. Make your calories cry.

All of these messages are so toxic, and I was finally starting to understand it. I was beginning to explore the concept of moving my body in ways that *felt good* and didn't need to have a time or mile marker associated with them.

My history with physical activity had always been all or nothing, where days of nothing happened once in a blue moon. I was always taking the hardest yoga classes with the toughest teachers. I **had** to leave each class feeling completely wrung out. In my mind, I had to be left energetically depleted to know that it "counted." Even on days where I felt exhausted or cloudy, my only solution was to move my body, be it a run or another sweaty, heated class. If I so much as considered skipping a day, my anxiety revved up and **God forbid** I hit traffic on the way or was running late to class. My whole persona would change.

I was constantly running from one thing to the next. My schedule was *always* packed from before sunrise to the time I went to sleep. I couldn't even entertain the idea or point of taking a relaxing or restorative yoga class. I even avoided going to new or different teachers for the sake of potentially wasting my time on a class that wasn't "enough of a workout."

Why would I waste my time doing that? That won't burn any calories.

I was rigidly structured and my body mimicked that. My body was hard in places it yearned to be soft. I kept telling myself I'd eventually slow down or take a day off, but I never did. Slowing down was something that created more anxiety and discomfort in my body since that's when my eating disorder thoughts would creep in. I had taken movement to the extreme, and I couldn't slow down.

I would wake up with physical activity on my mind and think about what I would do, when I would do it, and how I'd work my meals around it. This meticulous planning took over all my thoughts until I did it. Even then, while practicing or working out, I would already be thinking about the next day and time I would get to move my body. It was hell. It was suffocating. It was robbing me of life and my ability to *enjoy* moving and the million other aspects of life. I always wondered how people did it.

What would life be like if I didn't spend so much time moving? How much more time could I have spent with my family or friends or doing new things?

So much time. So much brain space.

Even though I had made improvements, I had not been able to take a full break from it. I honestly didn't believe in myself enough to think it was even possible for me. I had it so ingrained that without physical activity, my body would somehow not know what to do.

Those six weeks after surgery changed me. They changed what I knew was possible in my body and they changed the way I experience movement.

They helped me realize how much time I have in a day and how much creative energy I have left in me if I'm not out depleting it every day. The six weeks also gave me the confidence to know that my body is just fine without constant exercise. Movement and exercise are different. My body stills moves, even on days I don't exercise. We weren't meant to spend our days exercising, we were meant to find balance with movement as a way to support our life, not control it.

I now know that if and when there's another time in my life when I'm not as physically active or not able to be active at all, I'll be okay. That experience gave me the confidence I needed to release my fear. The truth is, we can do hard things, and they can be way easier than we imagined.

Something I also discovered after surgery was that it's okay to move my body without having a rigid intention or a set amount of time tied to it. It's okay to simply move and enjoy the physical sensations and joy it brings into my body. Physical activity doesn't have to drain us and deplete us; it can *fill us up* instead.

Taking a break and then allowing myself to ease back into exercise allowed me to experience all of this first hand. For me, I had to experience both extremes in order to find a healthy balance. I had to have a full break to be able to slowly start incorporating healthy movement back in. Movement is not wrong, but movement without freedom can be extremely crippling and damaging. Taking time off doesn't have to be forever. Do know that whatever it is you need, you will find it in moments of stillness.

Chapter 11

Rediscovering Yoga

Taking those six weeks off of exercise after surgery was the best thing I did for my yoga practice. As soon as I was medically cleared to move again, I had no desire to go back to practicing the same way I had been. My body was burned out and it took taking a break to realize it. The idea of navigating early afternoon traffic for 20 to 30 minutes to get to the studio, do an extreme, heated practice, and then get stuck in traffic again going back home was the last thing I wanted to do. Nothing about it sounded appealing.

Literally, none of it.

Taking time off of exercise helped me see how much time in my day I'd been dedicating to being physically active. When I stopped, I realized how much more time I had to do other things – to write, to be creative, to hang out with friends, to go shopping, to talk to my sister or mom on the phone. I had *so* much more time. Instead of starting back up right where I had left off with yoga, I started with slow, gentle home practices.

I still remember the day I got back home from a long day of meeting with cancer patients back-to-back. I walked into my quiet, cozy 600 square-foot apartment.

Full breath in. Full breath out. Finally some space and quiet. I took my work shoes off and allowed myself to feel the comforting texture of the light grey carpet under my feet. As if my body had suddenly gained awareness, I instantly felt the buildup of tension in my shoulders and the deep heaviness in my chest. I might as well have been carrying an extra-large box full of weights. I felt weighed down and stiff.

From my healing journey with my body and from building body awareness, I knew it was the stress and bottled-up emotions from my workday that I was feeling. It was refreshing to no longer jump to blaming my body for the heaviness I felt. I had learned that emotional heaviness does not equal physical heaviness, as much as it felt that way some days. Heaviness no longer meant I had "done something wrong." I was simply a human being having a physical experience. Something I learned quickly about working in a cancer clinic was that taking care of myself and allowing myself to feel and process all the emotional energy I took in during the day was crucial for me to continue to show up day after day. At that moment, I knew I needed something for myself. I needed to move the emotional energy out.

Without even changing out of my work clothes, I pulled out my thick, maroon yoga mat and laid it down in the small space between my dining room table and kitchen floor.

Down Dog.

I closed my eyes, pressed my hands into the mat, and allowed my chest to press back toward my thighs.

Crack. Pop.

The muscles in my back instantly released. *Mmmmm, space.* Keeping my eyes closed, I took a few deep breaths. With each exhale, I released every last bit of air out of my body, slowly allowing myself to release my day.

I spent another 5 to 10 minutes on my mat, breathing, moving, and feeling my muscles soften. Within minutes, I felt calm. Every single muscle in my body softened. I felt like me again. My shoulders no longer felt like they were cemented to my ears. I no longer carried the heaviness I had walked in with. The stillness within me finally matched the stillness and comfort of my quiet apartment. I didn't need a whole hour-long heated, structured, yoga class. I needed to slow down, feel, and breathe. With just a few minutes of space and silence, I was changed. It was so refreshing to give myself exactly what I needed in such a simple way without having to add in all the trouble of more driving and added stress.

*Wow. Could it be **this** simple?*

Could slowing down feel this good?

Slowing down and doing less yoga allowed me to start appreciating different areas of yoga and different tools for healing. Breathwork, meditation, inquiry, prayer, and reflection were mindfulness practices I had previously bypassed. I had always been so focused on my physical yoga practice that I hadn't found any interest in the mindfulness gems it provided or my moments of faith-based stillness.

On days where I would choose to do a longer practice, I noticed that I no longer wanted to push my body to a point of exhaustion. I didn't want to do a million yoga push-ups or hold a pose until it felt like my leg was going to fall off. If I was going to practice, I wanted to enjoy it. I wanted it to feel good.

I stopped practicing at the yoga studio I was attending and started exploring other teachers and other styles of yoga, which I had previously always sworn off due to a fear of them not being "hard enough."

One weekday evening, a friend invited me to join her in taking a class at a smaller, unheated studio. We walked in and were immediately greeted by a friendly instructor.

We started class slowly with combinations of poses I'd never done before. It felt like a fluid, coordinated dance. Suddenly, there we were mid-flow, moving one breath per pose totally in sync.

For the first time in a long time, I felt free and fluid in my body. I imagined it was what dancers felt like smoothly moving. After class, my friend and I joined the instructor for dinner. I instantly loved her. She was strong and fierce yet soft and intentional in her way of speaking and being.

"Don't tell anyone, but we're in the process of opening up a studio."

As soon as she shared that, something inside me lit up. I could sense that this evening wasn't the last time we'd connect. There was something about this studio and this woman that would have a part in my life. I didn't think much about it until we crossed paths again over a year later.

Her new studio was hosting their pre-opening classes and something in me felt called to go. I made it a point to show up to every single one. Not only did the same fluid, easeful practice speak to me, but so did the energy of the people and teachers in the room. There were no mirrors. It wasn't about comparison or structure. It was about yoga – from the heart, for the heart – just as their tagline read. I was instantly a raving fan and they didn't even know yet.

After one of the last classes, I waited 30 minutes for the room to clear out. There we were in the peaceful, plant-filled lobby, me and the same yoga instructor who had so beautifully introduced me to a fluid practice just over a year ago. I didn't think she even remembered who I was.

"I know you don't really know me, but what I do know is that everything in me is bringing me here. My heart wants and needs to be here."

"Well….are you teaching anywhere else right now?"

"No, I'm not. But I know I need to be here."

I wasn't taking no for an answer. I couldn't. My body wouldn't let me.

She looked at me, smiled, and said "Let me get your email and we'll set something up. You can audition."

I left that meeting somehow knowing that I'd be a part of the team. I could feel God guiding me, the same way I'd felt him guiding me in my healing journey. Everything in me knew this, and there was no questioning it. No more than a week and a half later, I was on their teaching schedule.

I was back into teaching and practicing yoga in a way that finally felt authentic and right for my body. I felt like I had finally found my place in the yoga world. I could give back to others what yoga had given me, and at the same time, support women in their own journey with their body, knowing and trusting that mindful awareness was the first step, or at least it had been for me.

My yoga journey continues to change and shift just as my life and body always have. The difference is that now I allow it. Nowadays, I find myself practicing less often, for less time, and mostly a slower, more intentional practice. There are days where 10 to 20 minutes in grounding poses is all I need. Then there are days where a faster, flowy class feels ideal. I have fallen in love with the variety and the ability to choose what serves me. I have fallen in love with the ability to work with my body, instead of against it.

Finding balance in my yoga practice and physical movement will be a forever practice. As my life changes, what my body needs changes too. What I am committed to is always choosing connection with others over control and rigidity. It is not always easy *and* it is what gets me to continue to grow into the person I wish to be; a person that is not a byproduct of a prior disorder. My work now is continuing to find the balance between what is challenging physically and what is too much. I have faith that God will always give me what I need, when I need it, whether it's a challenge to take time off or an opportunity to try something new. Movement is meant to change, and it's meant to be enjoyed.

Chapter 12

Our Body Knows Beauty

My sister and I were laying in our twin beds, barely four feet away from each other, and I was tired and dozing off. The only light still on was the dim light from the lamp on our wooden nightstand. We'd been having our nightly girl talk before bed, the kind we'd always had before my eating disorder came between us. I was fully engaged in the conversation until my eyelids started blinking shut. I don't remember what we were talking about, but I do remember how warm and calm I felt. Even though I had my eyes closed, I could feel my sister looking over at me as the faint light from our nightstand reflected off my pale skin. I could feel the warmth of her gaze. Before she even said it, I felt it.

"Lucia, you're so beautiful."

For the first time in a long time, I *felt* beautiful.

Our body knows beauty. I can't say I know what beauty feels like in your body, but I know what it feels like in mine. It's similar to the feeling I get when I'm outside on a gorgeous day. The gentle breeze of the wind cools my soft cheeks as they plump up when I smile. The sun reflects off my face only to beam back out into the world. My eyes are soft. My chest muscles are unrestrained and open, exposing my heart. My body feels as if it's effortlessly floating in space while a slight tingle of energy runs through my skin. I feel alive. I feel seen. I feel light. More importantly, I feel at peace.

Sometimes I wonder if feeling at peace allows us to feel beauty. When we're so busy and **in our heads**, do we even *pause* to appreciate the beauty that's right in front of us and *within us*?

All I know is that the moments in which I feel the most beautiful are the moments where I'm joyful and at ease. The moments I lock eyes with someone I love and see my reflection in their sweet gaze. The moments I take time to pray and feel God. The times I stare at myself in the mirror and sweetly remind myself of my beauty, imperfections and all.

Our body knows and feels beauty, not by how our body looks but by how our body feels.

The physical sensation of beauty is God's magical way of reminding us what it feels like to *be loved*. The way we feel it is the way He sees us. My nose isn't too big. My hips aren't too wide. My thighs aren't too thick. I am just right, exactly as I was made to be. As are you.

If our proportions create the physical space we take up, why would we make ourselves smaller? The more I come to accept the softer areas on my body, the more peaceful I feel. Whenever I am too structured, physically or mentally, that is when my anxiety takes over.

I might not know you, but I do know this:

Each one of us has our own beauty to share with the world, but we can't share it unless we see it for ourselves first. Our beauty is not limited by our body. It lives within us and through us.

I encourage you to get curious about the times in your life where you've felt beautiful, not from a physical definition but from a heartfelt sensation. Our beauty does not change as our body changes. It always resides within us. It is not something that can be taken away or changed by what society or people say. True beauty grows with time. It deepens as our relationships deepen. It shines as we pursue our purpose and passions. True beauty is forever. It is a feeling your body knows well. Allow yourself to feel it.

Chapter 13

Innate Intelligence

Our body not only knows beauty but also knows what it needs to survive and function well. Without energy, our body starts shutting down so that it can conserve as much energy as possible. It also shifts our attention completely toward food.

Why? Because it's trying to get our attention! It's trying to keep us alive.

It's very normal that the more we underfeed ourselves, the more obsessed we become with food – we might collect recipes, bake and cook for others, window shop at bakeries without getting anything, or even spend time browsing the grocery store for hours looking at different foods we won't allow ourselves to eat. It is one way our body tries to feed us mentally since we are not feeding it physically.

When I was underfeeding myself, I had no idea that my disordered rituals were common and that so many women who struggle with food and body image share interests and habits. We even have similar personalities.

Where are all my Type-A, go-getters? That's us, ladies!

Why is disordered eating so common among us?

For one, we love feeling in control and having structure. Combine that with what society tells us about food, our body, and our desire to be loved and accepted...and well, there you have it: disordered eating.

It's even common for dietitians to have had their journey and struggle with food, something I wish I would've known was normal. It wasn't until I shared my story that others felt comfortable sharing theirs with me. At the time, going through food struggles while being a dietitian made me feel like a fraud. I hated that everyone assumed I always had it all together. I didn't.

During my years of studying to be a dietitian, I was always intrigued by the definitions of each eating disorder. I subconsciously knew I had an issue, yet wasn't ready to admit it. I would read each definition and hear different parts of myself in each one. Because I never felt like I fit one definition, word for word, I would make it mean that my eating issues couldn't possibly be that bad – even though my habits and mindset were disordered. I would do things like cut food into small pieces or take really small bites; I'd move food around on my plate hoping I'd be able to buy time and eat less by doing so; I would only eat "healthy" or "lighter" versions of foods; and I would feel like my world was ending if I missed a day of working out. I was so familiar with my habits and weird eating rituals that I was easily able to notice which women around me were also struggling.

It's like a sixth sense to have the ability to feel someone else's struggle because you see your own in theirs. To this day, I can meet someone and know. There's a different energy someone carries with them when they are struggling with food and their body. It feels like an underlying barrier of disconnection and fear is present. I can see it in their eyes, just as my friend had seen it in mine.

As a clinician who now helps women ditch dieting and find freedom with food again, I see firsthand how many women trick themselves into believing that they are not "sick enough" or "bad enough" to get help. It doesn't matter if you are barely struggling or struggling to survive, you always deserve help. We don't have to wait until it gets "bad;" quite frankly the worse it gets, the more challenging it may be to come to terms with getting help. Eating disorders do a really good job of sucking us in and blinding us from reality.

Disordered eating and eating disorders distance us from the world.

They tune us out of our bodies and into our heads *so much so* that our body's natural signals go haywire. When we stop listening to our body, our body gives up communicating.

Not only do we get disconnected from our hunger, fullness, and satisfaction signals, but we also negatively impact our digestion. We start tricking ourselves into thinking we don't like certain foods because we're scared of them and what they'll do to our body. We start having trouble focusing. Our digestion slows. We get constipated, tired, and bloated. Our periods go missing or become extremely irregular. Our heart rate slows. We lose bone mass. We isolate ourselves. We live depressed and anxious. *The list is endless.*

Anyone can experience these struggles, even those who work in the wellness industry. Oftentimes, those of us who struggle the most are the ones in wellness spaces. I have empathy and understanding for anyone in these shoes as I have walked in them myself for years. The pressure to look fit and to eat a certain way can be extremely challenging, especially if you choose to work on your healing. It was no coincidence that in my healing journey, there was a period of time when the thought of being around fitness communities or spending time preparing or talking about "healthy meals" was the last thing I wanted to do. I was tired of living the "wellness life" and needed space, physically and mentally, to find a balance that worked for me. I needed to not be looked up to or looked at – at all.

After giving myself the time and space to redefine my definition of health and healthy habits, I slowly started integrating myself back into the wellness world. I didn't want to walk away from it; I wanted to be a catalyst for change within it. I was determined to find spaces where I could be myself and not be pushed to unhealthy extremes, places where I could create a shift in how we viewed and spoke about food and movement.

Allowing my body to change and to have others still see me show up was uncomfortable yet empowering. If I wanted women to feel accepted and comfortable in their bodies, I had to accept mine first. In order to show up, I had to allow myself to be a different version of myself than I had been before. I wanted to show up authentically and to be seen for who I was, not who I had been. I was tired of the wellness world portraying health as "perfect" bodies and "clean" eating. I wanted to start creating a healthier environment for anyone who was around me to feel empowered to take care of their body.

I started sharing. I was committed to letting women know that they were not alone and that diet rules and rigid physical activity routines didn't have to have a place in their life anymore. There was another way, and I was eager to help.

It was then that I realized I was not alone. God was giving me the opportunity to speak into the struggling hearts of others. If it hadn't been for my own struggles, I would've never been able to create that connection. The more I shared, the more connected I felt to other women and the more connected they felt to me. We had all been hurt by society, diets, and the rigidity of the fitness world. Now was the time to start healing.

Sharing keeps me on my path and allows others to discover theirs. The more we show kindness and compassion to ourselves, the more we cultivate it in others. It is not our words that make the biggest difference, it is how we show up for ourselves and others.

If one well-meaning decision to diet can negatively impact our lives forever, think about how much one well-meaning positive decision can put us on, *or back on*, the road to healing. Healing isn't linear; it's one hell of a roller-coaster ride. But the sweet moments – the ones where you get to share a pizza with your husband, celebrate with donuts and champagne after you get engaged, enjoy a slower morning without rushing to the gym, or see your body in the mirror and feel grateful for who you are and not what you see – are the moments that remind you that it is all worth it.

The sweetest breakthroughs often come right after times of deep struggle. I see it often and I've experienced it often. It's when we stick through the hard times and the never-ending challenges that break us open that we get to see and experience what's meant for us.

From my own experience and through working with women who have their own funky relationships with food and their bodies, I can tell you with 100% certainty that *it takes time*. We can't rush healing. It takes the exact amount of time it is meant to. What we *can* choose is when we get started. We might not ever fully feel ready to start our journey or to even continue with it, but we become ready when we choose it and not one second before. Recovery doesn't choose us, **we choose recovery** over and over again. It's not about being ready; it's about taking a leap of faith, even when we're scared to fail.

You are never "not sick enough" and your problem is never "too small" to ask for help. The more we surrender our struggles to God, the more He will guide us. *God gives us more than what we think we can handle because we're not meant to do this alone.* If we were only given what we could already handle, we'd never grow. The sooner we realize this and make the decision to stop tackling our challenges alone, the faster God sends us the exact people we need. Your healing journey is waiting for you and so are your people. If you are struggling, pause and listen: *what is the next step you are being called to take? What is there for you to do?*

Chapter 14

Trust Your Body, Change Your Life

Allowing my body to choose sounds like a weird concept, but it's my most authentic form of faith and intuition. God is constantly sending me signals and hints through my own body sensations. The more I listen and follow them, the more I find myself on a path that feels right.

I still remember the first time I started dreaming of my future in a way I hadn't before. I was almost two years into my healing journey with my body. My mind had gained the ability to look beyond irrational fears, something that I had not ever been able to do while constantly dieting.

When I started listening and trusting my body and intuitive knowing, my whole world opened up. I began to live and dream as if anything were possible. I gained confidence in setting aside thoughts like, "what if I fail and everyone thinks I'm a fraud" or "what if I'm not good enough" or "there's no way I can do that." Instead, I allowed my mind to swim through a sea of never-ending ideas. There was nothing to lose. I had already proven to myself that I could do hard things. If I could sit with my anxiety, allow my body to gain weight, and eat foods I thought I'd never be able to enjoy again, I could do *anything*. My eating disorder no longer had control over my life. While brainstorming, some ideas and aspirations came super quickly, while others were like creepy crawlers slowly inching their way toward me. They weren't visible unless I paused, paid attention, and allowed myself to explore.

I wanted to find the balance between feeling free and having structure in my life. I was craving a middle ground. That fall, I bought a planner called the *Make Shit Happen* planner. It was more than just a planner to help organize my life. It was a planner that created space for me to brainstorm, dream, and journal about what it was I wanted and what it was that was holding me back. It was the first time in my healing journey that I looked beyond my self-created limitations and dreamed BIG to create the life I wanted.

In the planner, I answered reflective questions and created curiosity lists about which hobbies I wanted to explore, which foods I wanted to try, which books I'd like to read, which places I'd love to explore, and what I would do if anything were possible.

I quickly found out that I couldn't be curious and judgmental about something at the same time. Our brain doesn't allow us to have two simultaneous thoughts at the exact same time. It is, however, *really* good at switching back and forth between thoughts which is why we can often feel stuck or confused. Choosing to be curious, instead of judgmental, allowed me to write things down without needing to achieve them. It freed me up. This was something I had done years prior with my dietitian through a food-curiosity list. I made a list of all the foods I wanted to enjoy along with a list of all the foods I was forcing myself to limit. The funny part was that the two lists were the same. *Go figure. I had been depriving myself of all the things I loved. No wonder I never felt satisfied.*

After creating my food lists, I slowly started adding my previously "off-limit" foods back into my life. It took time, repetition, and support, but I can now say my life is fuller because of it. There was nothing like rediscovering satisfaction and joy with food again, especially after not having experienced it in so long. The same happened with my life-curiosity list. The more I wrote down, the more excited and adventurous I felt. The minute we think or write down an idea that resonates with our soul, a light bulb goes off. For me, my whole body tingles. My eyes widen and my focus narrows. I feel it *everywhere*, even if it's only for a split second. My body knows. The same and opposite is true when we think of something that does not serve us. Our stomach may get queasy or sour. Our heart closes off. Our upper back stiffens. That's a firm no and we *feel* it.

Our body is *always* communicating with us and when something resonates, our body stores it. We might not be intentionally focused on achieving the big dream we crafted or the idea we had, but our body and subconscious mind are keeping track of it. They felt the idea. They saw it. The dream is there, and it's there to stay.

Every single time I've created a goal, made a vision board, or written down specifics about what I want, these things find their way into my life. It's not a mistake and it's not hocus-pocus magic. It's real. My gut knows what I need better than my mind, and my body sensations are always there guiding me and keeping me on my path. This level of body trust would have never been possible had I not done the healing work of slowing down and listening to my body. Trusting your body takes time, but it's worth it.

Becoming an intuitive eater changed my life. Not only did it teach me to listen to my body and honor what my body was asking for, with regard to food and movement, but also it allowed me to be intuitive in all areas of my life. Our body always knows. It's our mind that gets confused. There's something magical and inexplicable that happens when we allow our intuitive senses and subconscious brain to take over. Each time I allow myself to daydream, meditate, or be in prayer, I am shocked by the beautiful goals and ideas I create for myself and my life. Using the *Make Shit Happen* planner was the first time I fearlessly sat down to create my life, and I am so glad that I did.

In that planner, I dreamed of the business I would start, who I'd be serving, what foods I'd be eating, what my husband would be like, where I would travel, and what my ideal day would look like. Here I am, years later, living and creating that life. For me, that wouldn't have been possible if I hadn't started with food. My relationship with food was limiting everything in my life.

Before my healing journey, I was so focused on staying small that I never paused to ask myself what I wanted in life. All I valued was thinness and the life I believed it was attached to. By working through and releasing fear and worry, I was finally able to think *freely*. Once my eating disorder stopped taking over, my mind felt clear and open, as if nothing were out of reach.

The power of writing down what we want is the first step to creating a life we love. The second and most important step is ***believing*** we can achieve it. The third is taking action. Once I had my vision and goals written out, I started taking the steps I needed to get me moving toward them. As soon as I did, the right people started making their way into my life. Most of the time it felt completely random and unexpected, like the time I was looking for a roommate but ended up finding a life-long travel partner, or the time I needed professional financial advice and ended up meeting my now-husband. What I know now is that nothing is random. It all has a deeper meaning, even when we don't yet see it.

It has been five years since I started creating vision boards and writing big goals and it's not something I plan to discontinue anytime soon. Trusting my intuition, listening to God, and dreaming big allow me to stay open and free. They allow me to create my life with Him by my side. They keep me healed and remind me of the full life I get to live by not staying small.

If I ever find that I am limiting myself, living small, or living in fear, those are the times my eating disorder voice tries to come back in. It wants to promise me comfort in times of struggle or control in times of doubt. However, I now know better. All it ever fed me were lies.

I don't need my eating disorder to guide me or "keep me safe." I need

God. I need to trust and listen to what I know to be true. I need my authentic self and my drive to live. I need my body to survive and thrive the way it was designed to.

We don't always know how or when things will come into our life. We can, however, open up to our innate knowing and have faith that life is always happening just as it should be.

Writing down your dreams is like signing a paper contract with yourself. When your body knows you want it, it'll support you in getting it. *God will support you in finding it.* The dots will start to connect. Things will start to happen. Conversations will take place. Purchases will be made. And life-changing connections *will* occur.

If there's anything that healing has taught me, it's that the time is always now. Healing gives us the ability to live and dream in a way that otherwise wouldn't be possible, and it gifts us the confidence to jump right out of our comfort zone. It allows us to live a big life, instead of living one that shrinks our soul.

The longer we wait to choose healing, the more we miss out on life. The more we live in our heads, the more our physical sensations get shoved aside. If you are struggling with food, your body, or anything else, get clear on what your desired end result is. Pause and dream big. *What would be possible if anything were possible? What does it look like, what does it feel like, and who are you being in the world?*

Your healing journey might start with healing your relationship with food and your body, but it won't end there. You will likely heal parts of yourself you didn't even know needed healing. You may even discover a part of yourself you've never met: a part of yourself that lives life more fully than you ever thought was possible, a part of yourself that's stronger and bolder than anyone you've ever met.

When we work with the desires of our heart, there is no such thing as impossible. When we trust and listen, there is nothing to fear. There is only faith – living with you and within you. Let it all start to align. *Start trusting your body. It could change your life.*

Chapter 15

Your Body Always Knows

My healing journey taught me not only how to be intuitive with eating and movement but also how to be more intuitive in all areas of my life. Relationships being one of them. I had never paid much attention to the relationships in my life, or I should say I never paid much attention to all the things *that didn't feel right* about the relationships in my life.

I was so good at numbing out and covering up all uncomfortable emotions with my structured habits that I never faced anything that bothered me head-on. I let those things be background noise. As long as I got my run in and had eaten exactly what I wanted to, things didn't bother me as much.

As a result, my romantic relationships suffered. I had a lot of respect for myself but for some reason was okay with being treated poorly by men. I was really good at making up excuses for their behavior. I would be left hanging by a thread, waiting for a guy I didn't even like to text me back while sitting there making excuses for why he hadn't been able to. If they weren't interested, it simply meant I had done something wrong or I just wasn't good enough, which was another lie the eating disorder taught me. It made me believe I was never going to be enough. I had forgotten where my worth and value come from. I made myself believe that if I could achieve and maintain a "perfect body," then at least that would be enough.

During and after college, I was so interested in simply being accepted and feeling loved that I would put up with unacceptable behavior. It wasn't until I was in my healing journey that I started to see things differently, all while dating a man I thought I was going to marry. Our relationship was so dysfunctional. We were functional apart, just not together. We weren't a good match, and yet, I never took the time to fully admit it because being in a relationship felt easier than not being in one, especially after having dedicated so much time to it. In the first half of our relationship, I used my disordered habits to help me deal with all the anxiety and anger that came up from being in that relationship. If we argued, I'd run it off. If I felt neglected, shamed, or manipulated, I'd simply take some time by myself and find comfort in what I knew I could: structured and careful eating. That relationship was fueling my anxiety, and my unhealthy habits were helping me stay in it.

Throughout our whole relationship, something always felt off. I would choose to shake it off or run it off and told myself anything to help me stay in it like, "relationships are meant to be hard," "maybe things will change if we move in together," or the reason we always came back to during arguments "it was my fault." I had convinced myself that I was in love because I had gotten so good at ignoring all the bright blaring signs hitting me over the head. Once I started my healing journey, I convinced myself that no one else would be able to understand what I had gone through except for him. He was the one who experienced my hanger rages and emotional outbursts when I couldn't get in a workout and my anxiety would flare up. *Would anyone else be able to understand what I had and was currently going through?*

It wasn't until I started working on my relationship with food and finding other ways to care for myself that I started seeing how much of our relationship wasn't working. Our relationship wasn't challenging; it was *hard*. This is a difference I only understand now after being married to my person. There is a difference between someone challenging you or having hard relationship days versus being in a hard relationship that makes your whole life feel toxic.

We had talked about marriage several times. Superficially, I was excited. *I mean what young woman wouldn't be excited to know that there was someone out there who wanted to marry her?* Inside, though, I was crumbling. My body knew it wasn't for me. He wasn't for me, and I wasn't for him. Even though I couldn't pinpoint exactly what was off, I just knew something was not right. My body knew.

When we would spend time together, my anxiety would ramp up to the point where all I wanted to do afterward was go home and escape. Other than having major anxiety around him and with him, I constantly felt the need to get away. Physically, I ran. Emotionally, I was disconnected. I wasn't drawn to hold his hand in public or to be romantic with him at all, which if you know me now, I love being affectionate.

In my marriage today, as soon as Brett walks in, I jump out of my chair, run up to him, and greet him like I haven't seen him in years. I give him a strong, full-body hug allowing every cell in my body to melt as I smell the cologne on his neck. That was never there with my ex. It's chemistry that can't be faked.

My body didn't allow it because it didn't feel right. It didn't allow me to have the emotions or passion that I have now. Even though my body knew, my mind hadn't kicked in yet. I also had no idea how to communicate what I needed. The last thing I wanted to be was needy or complicated, even though not communicating my needs and thoughts didn't serve either of us. Considering our inability to properly communicate, our different ideas and values in life, and my underfed state, things weren't going well.

As I started working to eat more and move less, my hormones started to kick back in. I was more emotional and also more aware of what was bothering me. I started to feel again and man, were those emotions strong! Our arguments became more regular and more intense.

One day, after an argument, my body broke down, emotionally and physically. I was sitting on the light grey carpet in my bedroom, resting my body against the open bathroom door. My shoulders were slumped forward as I hugged my knees into my chest. My body was in a fetal position trying to keep itself together. I could feel the redness of my warm, puffy face. With tears streaming, I looked up at him. He was staring down at me with a confused look on his face. I couldn't tell if he were angry or annoyed. I had no words. Neither did he.

"*Well...*" he said finally. "*I have to go to work.*"

He walked out.

As soon as I heard the door close, I lost it. A fresh river of tears started flowing down my face. It felt like someone had just stabbed me in the chest, yanked out my bleeding heart, and thrown it away. I felt empty, as if the structure of my body were collapsing inward.

After a few minutes passed, I pulled myself up off the floor. I felt weak, but I took two steps into my bathroom, opened the shower curtain, and turned the shower to the hottest temperature it'd go. One leg at a time, I got in. As I stood there surrounded by steam, hot water hitting my body, I tightly closed my eyes, hunched over, both hands at my chest, and cried hysterically.

The pain that filled my body and my heart was so intense that I couldn't even hear myself cry. I *felt physically sick*. I wanted to hit something, purge, and scream all at the same time. I wanted it to end. I was tired of our arguments. I sat down in the tub and remember thinking to myself *this isn't normal; this isn't okay. I don't want to feel this way anymore. Why am I allowing this to happen?*

I knew then and there that I didn't want that to be my life. I didn't want to be in a relationship that made me feel like I was imploding. I couldn't stop ignoring what my body was saying to me. I had to get out of it. I had to break free.

Chapter 16

When You Know, You Know

It took being in a relationship that wasn't for me to become clear on exactly what I wanted and what I would refuse to settle for. Many years into my healing journey, there we were, Brett and I, sitting at a small square table with white linens. I was wearing my striped white and grey silky tank top, black high-waisted shorts, and my dressier, black sandals.

"Let's do oysters," he said.

"Oh, I've never had oysters."

"You'll love them; let's start there."

I was half a glass of red wine in when they brought the oyster tray over. I remember thinking to myself, "*Well, here's to trying new things and being flexible.*" One of the things recovery gifted me was the ability to go out to dinner and try new foods. I could be present with the person I was with versus in my head thinking about what I was about to eat.

There we were, at our first dinner date together. A dinner date I had turned down several times earlier that day. I remember being on a walk in the park next to my apartment when my phone rang. It was Brett calling *again*. He asked me what I was doing, even though he had asked multiple times that day, what my day would be like. I'd told him I wasn't interested in dating, not because I didn't want to date him but because I was finally feeling like myself after so many transitions within the last year: a move across the city, ending my old relationship, finding comfort in my own body. There had been so much freaking change that I was craving slowing down, observing, and relaxing.

"So what are *you* up to tonight?" I asked him.

"Well, I wanted to go out to dinner with this girl, but she keeps turning me down."

I laughed. Brett always has a way of getting me to laugh that warms my heart. It makes me feel connected to him in such a way that it feels like we've known each other for years.

"You *really* want to go out to dinner, *don't you?*"

"Yeah, it'd be fun. It's not a big deal unless you make it one."

I laughed and couldn't help but agree. "Okay, let's go! Just as long as we keep it simple. I don't want anything fancy."

"Perfect."

Fast forward 30 minutes into our meal, oysters were on the table, my glass of red wine half full. I could feel my heart slowly starting to open up. We started talking about where we were in our lives and how we felt about relationships. Something about his sweet stare, warm smile, and persistence made me feel at home in my skin.

Out of nowhere, I jumped right to the point, "*Okay...so what are your non-negotiables?*" knowing that if I asked him, he'd have to ask me back. To this day, I don't remember exactly what he said, but what I know is that as soon as he started answering my question, I felt something inside of me light up. My whole body felt lighter and calm. I felt trust and connection. There was light, easeful energy moving between us. It was then, while staring right into his eyes, that I felt the thought land right into my body...*I could marry this guy.*

Ummmm, woah. Where did *that* come from?

It wasn't the wine, ladies. It was God. It was God allowing us to share space, stare into each other's eyes, and see the future. It was God connecting two bodies that were meant for each other. *When you know, you know.* I had never understood that until that moment. Even though that moment was a glimpse of what was to come, I didn't think about it much at that time. My body, however, recorded it. It knew what was coming.

It's moments like these that change our lives. We get a sweet glimpse of our future whether we choose to acknowledge it or not. Our body is always keeping track of what's meant for us.

My relationship with Brett has always felt easy, even when it's been challenging. Being 150% opposite, we don't always agree with each other. There are moments where we need space or moments where we just stare at each other because neither of us knows what to say. The thing is, even when I'm angry or upset, there's still love. Love, not as a feeling, but as a deeper inner knowing.

On our wedding day, there was nothing more beautiful than having those tall brown doors open up before me so that I could lock eyes with him for the first time. Walking down that long aisle was one of the most beautiful and impactful moments of my life. I was easefully floating through space, overwhelmed with joy and love as I looked into the eyes of the man that would be beside me for the rest of my life. Even God was smiling.

Our bodies now know each other. There's not a day that I can't sense him – where he is, what he's feeling, what he needs. He's my partner and my *soulmate*. He's the person I've shared my whole being with and my body knows it.

God placed Brett on my path when I was ready. If I would've met him earlier in life, I wouldn't have had the awareness or the maturity I needed to get to know him. That's how life works. That's how God works. Don't ever be with someone out of fear of not finding your person. Don't ever settle for what you know and feel isn't right. Trust yourself. Trust your gut. It knows true love, which is deeper than a fleeting feeling. It's a vow. It's knowing that God brought you two together and intersected your paths for a reason.

It wasn't by coincidence that, as soon as I was in a healthier place with my body, God handed me the man I would marry. I now had the capacity to love and trust someone else because I had learned to love and trust myself. I wouldn't have been ready for or known how to ask for what I wanted had I not had years of healing beforehand. I healed my eating disorder, yeah, but I also healed my confidence, my faith in my intuition, and my ability to love and be loved.

Chapter 17

Sharing My Soul

Deciding to marry Brett was the easiest decision I've ever made. Probably because from the moment we started dating, our bodies knew. Our souls knew. Marriage felt like a natural progression of our relationship that I can't even pinpoint the exact moment when we started talking about it. What I do remember very clearly was the day I told Brett I was a virgin. It was one of the conversations we had that continued to solidify that he was meant for me in every way.

Being a virgin at 29 was not something I shared with most people. Why? Because every single time I told someone that, I was looked at as if there were something wrong with me. Women would feel sorry for me and men would see it as a burning red flag, something to steer clear of. It was the reason most men said they "couldn't" date me.

As if sex were the only thing I was good for?

Staying a virgin in a long-term relationship was challenging. It was one of the things my ex-boyfriend had struggled with. It was the main cause of numerous arguments that always left me feeling insecure. He would use "sexual tension" as a reason why he'd blow up. I mean, I get it, and at the same time, dude, figure yourself out.

I mean, hello? What would he do the day I delivered a baby and couldn't have sex for six to eight weeks or if one of us got sick? What then? Would he then not be able to be with me?

Now, having had sex, as much as it's super fun, I don't believe it replaces all other ways to connect or be intimate with each other. One of the things

I love most about our marriage is that we got to build a strong foundation without it. Our connection in dating wasn't based on the physical, which I truly believe made me feel empowered and secure. He didn't love me for my body. He loved me for me.

From the time I was in middle school, I had made a promise to myself and to my future husband that I would wait. I saw sex as sacred. If I could create a human being from having sex with someone, I wanted it to be with my husband. Call me conservative. Prudish. Weird. I've heard it all. I just always knew what felt right for me and stuck to it.

Maybe one of the positive things that did come out of my eating disorder was being more mindful of sharing my body, even if in many other ways it didn't serve me. Giving my whole self to my husband felt like I got to come full circle in my journey of honoring and listening to my body. Not only was I now caring for my body differently, but also I was trusting enough to share it with someone else. It was a symbol of our union and the body that would one day carry our future child.

When I first told Brett I was a virgin, we were barely in the "talking" stages of our relationship. You know, the one where they call you and text you all the time, and each time you see their name on your phone, you drop everything you're doing and act super calm as you pick up the phone...even though every cell in your body is dancing up and down? That fun stage.

I had barely finished parking my car when I saw the phone ringing. Brett Harmeling calling. The biggest dorky smile spread across my face. The look a little girl gets when you offer her a big colorful lollipop. My cheeks puffed up like two soft balloons, and I immediately put my car in park and took a deep breath.

"Hey, how's it going?" I asked.

He asked how my day was and how I was doing. In the middle of our flirty conversation, he made a sarcastic sexual remark. I laughed.

"*Yeah*, it's been a while," Brett said.

I paused and laughed. "You have no idea!"

He laughed.

I was not about to get into that conversation with someone I had barely started dating. "Maybe that's a conversation for another time..."

"Are you a virgin?"

"Uhhhh...well...yeah. Yeah, I am."

I waited to see what ridiculous and demeaning response I'd get this time.

"Okay. Cool. That's awesome."

Wait, what?! No rude remark? No freak-out moment?

"Oh? That's it?" I asked.

"Yeah...I mean I wanted to wait but it just didn't work out."

"Oh. Cool."

We kept chatting as I walked into my furniture-less apartment that I had only recently moved into, opened up the blinds allowing the sun to shine in, and sat on the hardwood floor.

"I'm really surprised you're not freaking out right now."

"Why would I? If we're meant to be, it's not going to take us *that long* to figure it out."

Another one of those moments. I don't know if it was the sun brightly shining into my apartment, the peace I felt in my body, or the realization that a relationship could be and feel so differently from what I was used to – it just felt *right*. In my soul. My heart. My body.

A year later, we got engaged and six months after that we got married. Pay attention to how someone makes you feel. Actions and words are meaningful, but the physical sensations you feel tell you everything. Tune in, your body already knows.

Chapter 18

The Truth Behind Body Image

Body image is still hard for me sometimes. It's the last thing to improve when healing your relationship with food and your body. I can be eating all the fun foods, moving my body intuitively, living life well, yet all of a sudden I wake up and feel icky. I still have these days. Days where I don't want to be in my body or days where initially all I can feel is the heaviness within me. Days where nothing feels good on and the more I go through my closet, the more upset I become. Days where it's easier not to show up for an event and be seen than to talk myself into going. Days where it takes me forever to get ready. When I'm in this place, I'm living in my head and making everything about myself wrong.

I find that these days happen more frequently when big changes are happening in my life: I launch something big in my business; I write my whole story for it to be read by thousands, if not millions, of women; I present to a big crowd; or it's the holidays and I'm surrounded by family for hours on end. In all of these scenarios, I am allowing myself to be seen.

These are the days my eating disorder tries to creep back in with unrealistic and unsustainable solutions. It's no surprise this happens since my go-to for managing emotions for over ten years was restriction and excessive exercise.

Being able to distinguish the eating disorder voice from my own has been life-changing. I can have a bad body-image day, yet not allow that voice to take over. I don't have to do what my thoughts tell me to do and I don't have to believe every thought I have. Thoughts are just thoughts. Some are helpful and some are not.

The best thing I can do when I'm having a bad body-image day is not to focus on my body because the more I do, the more I'll be tempted to change it. Instead, I focus on other things: my business, my clients, my marriage, or prayer – the things that having a body allow me to have and do in this world.

When I ask myself what it is I need and how I can care for myself, my answer usually includes kind thoughts, comfortable clothes, satisfying meals, and lowering my perfectionist expectations for the day. We aren't meant to feel comfortable in our bodies every single day. That isn't the goal. The goal is to find a way to be in our body, care for ourselves the best we can with what we have, and live out our purpose, regardless of how we think we look. How we feel does not have to dictate our lives. How we act and how we show up is what makes the biggest difference.

Chapter 19

Where My Body Has Led Me

I used to not understand why God "gave me" an eating disorder. Even to this day, when I say or type that out, it feels off. *God doesn't give us bad things, does He?* It wasn't until a few years ago that I realized what a blessing my eating disorder has been for my life. Let me guess – not what you expected to hear? *Girl, same.*

It sounds backward, yet it has been the most anchoring experience so far. It has made me, **me**. It has led me to my profession, my love of yoga, my ability to understand and teach others about their own bodies, my inner knowing and understanding of my intuition, and my deep relationship with Christ.

My healing process started way before I even knew I was healing. God was slowly placing life-changing keys and people in my life at the exact times I needed them. I didn't realize how much of my life was happening on purpose and *right on time* until years later. In fact, all of it was. The smallest decision to do or not to do something or even randomly meet someone can change our lives forever. Something that has become more and more apparent to me now as an adult is this: the people God puts right in front of us are not there by accident, even the ones who annoy and challenge the heck out of us. Especially them, they are *just* as important in our journey.

It's pretty magical to think about all the things that have to go right and all the decisions that have to be made and not made to have two people end up in the same place, at the same time next to each other.

Life is on purpose. There are <u>no</u> mistakes. *So, did God give me an eating* *disorder?* I don't think of it that way. I think God knew I'd struggle with one, so instead, He sent me everything and everyone I would need to help me and support me in my journey. I believe the same for you, no matter what your struggle is.

Whatever God wants to give through you, He will give to you first. As soon as I heard this, my soul connected to it. I'd always had an inkling that God would lead me to work with women who have disordered relationships with food. Each time the thought came up, I'd dismiss it because I knew deep inside that I just wasn't there...*yet.*

I never thought my journey was special until now. I sit here, tears rolling down my face, just thinking about the blessing it has been to experience deep struggle. To have days where I felt so lost and so lonely in my head that I never thought freeing myself was possible. To have days where I would get so angry with God because I was carrying these struggles.

Why me? *Why can't I be like other women? Why does everything have to feel so hard?*

I get it now. To find balance for myself, I had to play with the extremes. Not everyone goes through that, but I did. It's been my journey. I wouldn't have the compassion or understanding I do now if I hadn't struggled through the tremendous pain I did during recovery. I had to sit with myself in my loneliest moments.

God has led me my entire life. Going through my healing journey taught me so much about how to listen and trust my body that there was no way it wouldn't have changed my life. The more I chose to listen to my body and heal my relationship with it, the more my life started to make sense. I started having a sense of fulfillment and ease in trusting the journey and trusting that each and every single step was meant to happen.

Learning to trust my body started with feeding myself enough to where my body was no longer solely focused on food. I was then able to think of other things, be creative, be adventurous, dream, and spend time with others while being fully present.

Not only did I start having a more ease-filled relationship with hunger and fullness, but also I started having a less fearful and resistant relationship to hunger in all realms. Spiritual hunger. Career hunger. Relationship hunger. Instead of aiming for temporary fullness, I started aiming for *satisfaction*.

Each day I walked into the job where I was no longer meant to be, I started to feel intense physical sensations throughout my body. The heaviness in my step. The tightness and rigidity in my shoulders. The dullness in my stare. I became aware of how I was cruising, and not the relaxing, enjoyable kind. The kind of cruising that you do when you're mentally checked out and don't even realize what you've missed seeing while you're driving home. *I was missing out on a lot.*

It has been three years since I left my clinical job, and even though I don't have it all figured out yet, I know and trust that God continues to lead me. I don't need certainty; I need faith.

Giving up a secure job with secure benefits and jumping into a world of uncharted possibilities was scary, but not scarier than living my life unfulfilled and numb. My business has and continues to be shaped by the women who support it and have helped it come to life. I don't always know what I'm doing, but I've come to know that my body always does. When I'm not sure what's next, I pray. I listen. I spend time in silence and with others.

I trust that my journey is not over. My life, intuition, and journey with my body will continue to shape themselves as my life continues to unfold. I do know that I wouldn't be where I am today, writing this book, if it weren't meant to be.

I'm sharing my story so that you know you are not alone. We're all in this together. This life is not about being perfect. It is about sharing our imperfections and knowing that in being vulnerable and relatable, we get to be one piece in someone else's puzzle of healing.

Chapter 20

Gratitude

My journey has been full of ups and downs, but I wouldn't change it for anything. It has led me to be here, writing this book, sharing authentically, and knowing that it's better to do it scared than not to do it at all.

I'd love to tell you that today I never have a bad body-image day or food struggle, but that wouldn't be real. My journey with food and my body is constantly changing and evolving. It flows with the flow of my life. There are good days and bad days, high highs and low lows.

The beautiful part about this is that throughout my journey of body trust and respect, I get to have faith in the process. I know that my body will continue to change for the rest of my life. I will get pregnant, give birth, get pregnant again, give birth again, and go through hard times, joyful times, and everything in between. My body is resilient. It was made to change. It was made to have an impact, not just physically, but spiritually.

Without my intuition, I wouldn't be where I am now in my business, creating one day at a time by praying and listening to my inner knowing. The same inner knowing that brought me to write this book. Even when things don't make sense logically or financially, but they make sense spiritually, I listen. I've gotten to a point where when I know, *I know* and there's no denying it. I also know when my mind and body are overwhelmed because I've hit decision fatigue and simply need a break from all of it. I especially know when I'm holding back on doing something out of fear. My body feels it. My heart loses its spark.

The reason I create a yearly vision board for my life is because it allows me to dream big. I write down goals so my eyes can see them and my body can sense them. By writing them down, I create a spiritual contract with myself, one that my body knows not to break.

I am creating a world where women don't feel alone: a world where women feel seen and supported, where they recognize their potential as well as the things that hold them back. When we get clear on what we want and what we don't want, we are more likely to choose what we do want. *It can be that simple.*

Me? I choose recovery. I choose freedom. Laughs. Fun nights with my husband. A cycle that supports my fertility. The satisfaction that comes with eating a delicious slice of bread or a yummy plate of pasta or ice cream late at night. I chose it then and I choose it now. There's more to life than my body. There is what I get to do with it and what I get to share through it. If there's one piece of advice I wish to leave you with, it's this: have faith in the process and in your body. You are exactly where you are meant to be. You are constantly being guided on your path. Listen more, do less, and don't ever miss out on connecting with others because of food, exercise, or how you feel in your body. You deserve to be seen, loved, and appreciated just as you are.

Keep reading. Keep sharing. Keep living.

With love,

Lucia

About the Author

Lucia Harmeling believes the body is a vessel through which we experience life. It is by trusting our body that we transform our life. As a Body Attunement Dietitian, Certified Intuitive Eating Counselor, registered yoga instructor, Board Certified Dietitian in Oncology Nutrition, and eating disorder survivor, Lucia knows firsthand the power and life-changing impact of nourishing the body both physically and mentally. When Lucia isn't busy writing, she is speaking in front of groups of women, leading workshops, and working with women one on one in their journeys with food and their body. Lucia was recognized as the Young Dietitian of the Year in 2018 and 2019 and continues contributing and serving in her work, creating a huge impact.

Lucia resides in Houston, Texas, with her husband, Brett, and their lovely pit bull, Roxy. She enjoys strong coffee, eating satisfying foods, reading inspiring books, spending time outside, and moving her body in ways that feel good.

Women Supporting Women

To all the incredibly talented women in my life, thank you for helping me create this book.

Artist:

Haley Bowen is a figurative artist who strives to empower women through nude portraiture. Drawing nude figures for over 15 years, Haley is a platform for visual storytelling through her lyrical linework, specific color palette, and intimate drawing experiences. Hosting hundreds of drawing sessions for women of all colors, body types, ages, and backgrounds, Haley uses art to rebuild the relationship between the physical body and the woman within. Haley has a studio in Houston, Texas. Follow her on Instagram @ haleybowenart and learn more by visiting www.haleybowen.com.

Graphic Designer:

Stephanie DuBois is a graphic designer and art director in Houston, Texas, focused on bringing people's visions for their brands and initiatives to life. Learn more about her creative work and process at stephaniedubois.com.

Editor:

Michelle Gean, a former Elephant Journal Editor and current freelance writer and book editor, helps writers birth their books into the world. Books have the ability to push the bounds of what we have previously viewed as "possible" as they take us out of the limited confines and perspective of our meat suits. To see the world from a million different perspectives and challenge the norms and structures we live within is why Michelle does the work that she does. When she's not immersed in words, she can be found running up mountains in Boulder, Colorado. Follow her on Instagram @ michelle.gean.

Resources

Books

Life without Ed – Jenni Schaefer

Intuitive Eating – Evelyn Tribole, Elyse Resch

The Intuitive Eating Workbook – Evelyn Tribole, Elyse Resch

Body Kindness – Rebecca Scritchfield

Health at Every Size – Linda Bacon

Anti-Diet – Christy Harrison

The Gifts of Imperfection – Brene Brown

The Intuitive Eating Guide to Recovery – Meme Inge

Podcasts:

Food Psych – Christy Harrison

Nutrition Matters – Paige Smathers

Websites:

National Eating Disorders Association – Nationaleatingdisorders.org

Intuitive Eating – www.intuitiveeating.org

Made in the USA
Coppell, TX
17 May 2021

55857386R00079